SCHOLASTIC
ART & WRITING AWARDS
PRESENTS

THE BEST TEEN WRITING OF 2017

Edited by
Trace DePass
2015 Scholastic Awards
Gold Medal Portfolio Recipient

For information or permission, contact:
Alliance for Young Artists & Writers
557 Broadway
New York, NY 10012
artandwriting.org

Editor: Trace DePass
Managing Editor: Hannah Jones
Director, Programs: Debra Samdperil
Design Director: Meg Callery
Production Manager and Proofreader: Jean-Paul Bass
Copy Editors: Ingrid Accardi and Mel Wohlgemuth
Production Assistant: Tommy de Yampert

Front and back cover: *Tropicana* and *Loves Me Not*,
Printmaking by Bronwyn Katz, Grade 12, Age 18,
Paideia School, Atlanta, GA

Inside front and back cover: *Ocular Phantasm*, Drawing & Illustration by Wah Ka Soe, Grade 11, Age 18, Omaha Benson Magnet High School, Omaha, NE

Anthology printing, August 2017
ISBN13: 978-1-338-25624-6
ISBN10: 1-338-25624-6

DEDICATION

The Best Teen Writing of 2017 is dedicated to Paul Chan, who received a Scholastic Art Award in 1992, while a high school senior in Omaha, Nebraska. He was recently presented with the 2017 Scholastic Awards Alumni Achievement Award. He has gone on to create an internationally acclaimed body of artistic and literary work. Chan is renowned for his legacy of creating boundary-pushing work that addresses some of the most pressing issues of our time, including antiwar activism, environmental issues, and matters of human rights.

Chan received the Hugo Boss Prize in 2014, which coincided with his solo exhibition *Nonprojections for New Lovers* at the Solomon R. Guggenheim Museum in New York in 2015. He is the founder of Badlands Unlimited, a press that publishes e-books, limited-edition paper books, and artist works in digital and print form. Chan is represented by Greene Naftali in New York.

TABLE OF CONTENTS

Journalism

Novel Writing

Personal Essay & Memoir

Poetry

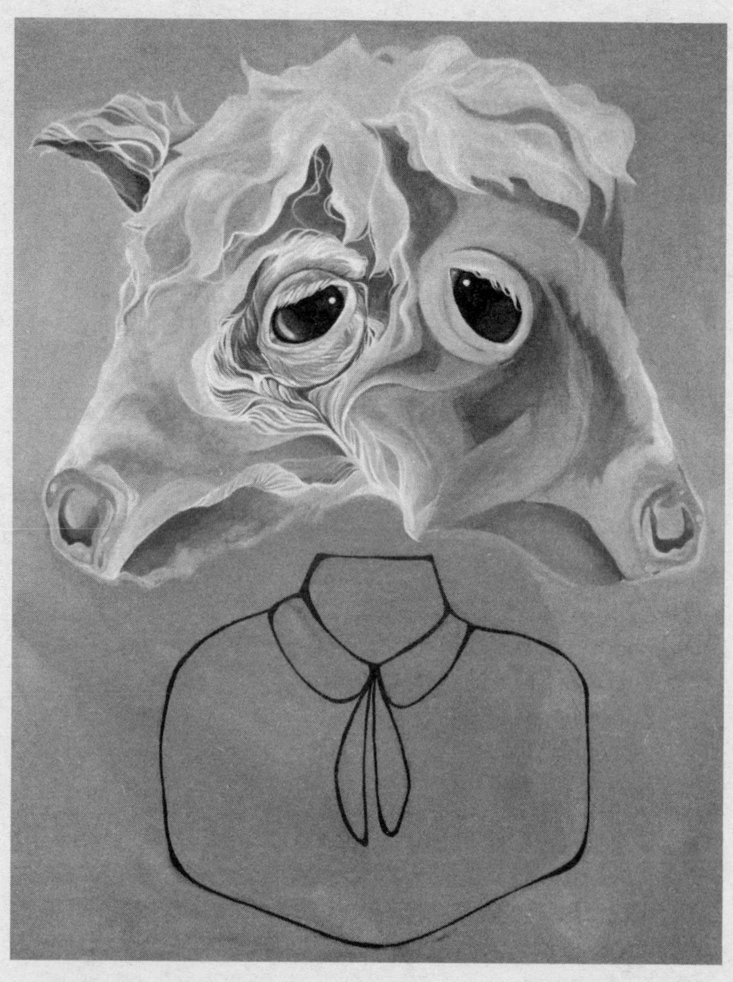

PEYTON BARNES, ***Polycephaly***, Grade 12, Age 17. Deep Run High School, Glen Allen, VA. Michael Guyer, *Educator*

ABOUT THE BEST TEEN WRITING OF 2017

The pieces featured in *The Best Teen Writing of 2017* were selected from works that earned National Medals in the 2017 Scholastic Art & Writing Awards. The Scholastic Awards, a national program presented by the Alliance for Young Artists & Writers, identifies and showcases teenagers with exceptional artistic and literary talent. Founded in 1923, the program celebrates the accomplishments of creative students and extends opportunities for recognition, exhibition, publication, and scholarships.

This year, 791 students earned National Medals in writing categories. The works selected for this publication represent the diversity of the National Medalists, including age and grade, gender, genre, geography, and subject matter. They also present a spectrum of the insight and creative intellect that inform many of the pieces.

A complete listing of National Medalists and online galleries of awarded works of art and writing can be found on our website, **artandwriting.org**. Visit our site to see how to enter the 2018 Scholastic Art & Writing Awards, as well as a list of our scholarship partners and ways you can partner with the Alliance to support young artists and writers in your community.

Some of the writing selections have been excerpted. Go to **artandwriting.org/galleries** to read all of the work as it was submitted.

ABOUT THE SCHOLASTIC ART & WRITING AWARDS

Since 1923, the Scholastic Art & Writing Awards have recognized the vision, ingenuity, and talent of our nation's youth, and provided opportunities for creative teens to be celebrated. Each year, increasing numbers of teens participate in the program and become a part of our community—young artists and writers, filmmakers and photographers, poets and sculptors, video game artists and science fiction writers—along with countless educators who support and encourage the creative process. Notable Scholastic Awards alumni include Andy Warhol, Sylvia Plath, Cy Twombly, John Baldessari, Ken Burns, Kay WalkingStick, Richard Avedon, Stephen King, Luis Jiménez, Paul Chan, Marc Brown, Truman Capote, and Joyce Carol Oates—to name just a few.

Our Mission

The Scholastic Art & Writing Awards are presented by the Alliance for Young Artists & Writers. The Alliance is a 501(c)(3) nonprofit organization whose mission is to identify students with exceptional artistic and literary talent and present their remarkable work to the world through the Scholastic Art & Writing Awards. Through the Awards, students receive opportunities for recognition, exhibition, publication, and scholarships. Students across America submitted nearly 331,000 original works during our 2017 program year across 29 different categories of art and writing.

Our Programs

Through the Scholastic Awards, teens in grades 7–12 from public, private, or home schools can apply in 29 categories of art and writing for a chance to earn scholarships and have their works exhibited and published. Beyond the Awards, the Alliance for Young Artists & Writers produces a number of programs to support creative students and their educators, including the Art.Write.Now.Tour, the National Student Poets Program, the Scholastic Awards Summer Workshops and Scholastic Awards Summer Scholarships programs, the Golden Educators Residency, and many more. The Alliance publications feature works by National Medalists of both art and writing in our annual National Catalog. Additionally, we publish a collection of exemplary written works in this anthology, *The Best Teen Writing,* and a chapbook that features works from the National Student Poets. These publications are distributed free of charge to schools, students, educators, museums, libraries, and arts organizations across the country.

2017 SCHOLASTIC ART & WRITING AWARDS NATIONAL WRITING JURORS

American Voices

Sylvia Acevedo
Alexandria Ang
James Walter Doyle
Thom Duffy
Joshua Furst
Amy Hausmann
Varian Johnson
Melissa Miles
Gholnecsar Eushena Muhammad
Michael Northrup
Gerald Padilla
Roger Sutton

Best-in-Grade

Dudley Brier
Paige Cornwell
Abigail Donahue
Rebecca Hahn
Betty Harris
Lynn Harris
Carol Kellerman
Jessica Lee
Loretta Lopez
Lisa Schulman
Julien Terrell
Rich Wallace

Critical Essay

Marlene Graham
Catherine Lacey
Sergio Troncoso

Dramatic Script

Jeffrey Harper
Jen Longo
Topher Payne

Flash Fiction

Stacey Lee
Maggie Thrash
John Corey Whaley

Gedenk Award for Tolerance

Dev Aujla
Monis Khan
Pat Schmatz

Humor

John Elnathan
Stephanie Gadlin
Sue Wolf

Journalism

Brandon Benavides
Kris Higginson
Mohana Ravindranath

New York Life Award

Lauren Beukes
Karen Marie Moning
Vynetta Morrow
Rollo Romig

Novel Writing

Da Chen
Tendai Huchu
Amie Kaufman

Personal Essay & Memoir

Randy Brown
Edwidge Danticat
Shannon Gibney
Cara Jensen
Amy Newmark
Duvall Osteen

Poetry

Mahogany Browne
Teri Cross Davis
Emily Garcia
King Grossman
Marie Jaskulka
Timothy Liu
David Tomas Martinez

The RBC "Flaunt It" Award

Danielle Bennett
Gabriel Magraner
Baratunde Thurston

Science Fiction & Fantasy

Tim Floreen
Nicole Kornher-Stace
Naomi Novik

Short Story

Chris Bachelder
Jennifer Mathieu
Katie McGinnis
Cammie McGovern
Lavanya Sankaran

Writing Portfolio

Moira Bailey
J.C. Carleson
Marie Jaskulka
Michelle Koufopoulos
Mildred Rias
Luis Rodriguez
Jeff Shotts
Eileen Tabios

EDITOR'S INTRODUCTION

Trace DePass
2015 Scholastic Awards
Gold Medal Portfolio Recipient
2016 Teen Poet Laureate for the Borough of Queens

Perhaps what tethers this book beyond its spine is an ever-present demand for answers, each writer telling their story without being silenced. Perhaps there might be a particular joy in unpacking, relinquishing, nearly deflecting the endless inquisitions made on these writers' intersecting identity. These writers hold "they" whom hold power accountable. And these young minds are wondering whom power might sacrifice next.

As one essayist offers a shattering lens to the "American Dream" for people of color, motioning that perhaps this dream is a lie cloaked in the narrative of equal opportunity, another essayist then asks: How can pain and relief coexist? And a poet implies we hold space for joy as a response despite grief, as she captures herself pirouetting throughout the kitchen, alongside her mother. Meanwhile, a playwright depicts a former counselor in dialogue with his therapist over the death of his own mother, who had abandoned him as a boy.

Not unlike Ray Bradbury, a science fiction writer imagines how artificial intelligence might become autonomous and sentient, and what it might do to survive and maintain power. Another essayist mentions our current president's use of social media, today's search engines that rapidly spread misinformation, our human obsession with life online, and our dependence on our phones.

All of this is to say, these writers are doing the work of researching their own lives, creating art derived from urgent observation while having to participate in their macro and micro worlds. However, while under attack and surveillance, kids these days are watching themselves, and watching particularly inside themselves. Intermittently, they remind us that the subjective is not inherently untrue; that allegory, the personal narrative, their art and world contrived from it, are all revolutionary proof. They are definitely onto something here.

In 2017, this anthology cannot be any less than labor itself, tired of the capitalist system that perpetuates it; a document that aims to laughingly make concise our many grievances, existential or otherwise. One Gold Medalist asks of a loved one, who dangles at the tip of their investigation, "What reason do we have to live?" And yet collectively they beg the question "For what reason do we have to die?"

SAM ZANOWSKI, ***Space Station***, Grade 12, Age 18, Wauwatosa East High School, Wauwatosa, WI. Kelly Frederick Mizer, *Educator*

GOLD MEDAL PORTFOLIO

Graduating high school seniors may submit a portfolio of four to eight works for review by authors, educators, and literary professionals.

The eight recipients of the Gold Medal Writing Portfolio each receive a $10,000 scholarship.

Some of the writing selections have been excerpted. Visit **artandwriting.org/galleries** to read all of the work as it was submitted.

Sun Goddess

ZAINAB ADISA, Grade 12, Age 17. Pittsburgh CAPA School,
Pittsburgh, PA. Mara Cregan, *Educator*

I am newly seven and, the relationship between
melanin and the amount of sunlight
that seeps into my pores is unknown.

She is a cool coal color,
The dark-purple stain left on your fingers
from blackberry residue.

Back then I still stray away
from shade. Because my top priority is
to soak in the sun's glory and become a Goddess.

Her full lips part and out comes the sentence,
"You are already dark enough."
Suddenly the sun no longer feels God-like
on my skin as I try to comprehend what it's like to be
"too dark." Because as a seven-year-old, who knew
there was a scale, in which hue determined
beauty, and beauty
represented the amount of love one could receive.

And while I am still trying
to understand all of this I hear my friends laugh wildly,
though it is more of a chuckle that quickly dies
into Cuyler: (the boy whose aunt would sometimes watch me)
telling Monet Jones to shut up.

This feels like a burst of heat
exploding into waves, running across my body.
He tells me I am not "too dark."

ABCD: American-Born Confused Desi

ZARA BATALVI, Grade 12, Age 16. Thomas Jefferson High School for Science and Technology, Alexandria, VA. Jill Burdick-Zupancic, *Educator*

In Pakistan, there is a phrase for people like me: ABCD. An American-Born Confused Desi. Usually a slur, the label refers to the children of South Asian immigrants who have been ethnically "confused" by their clashing Western and Desi upbringing. They speak Urdu, but they pronounce the words wrong. They know the lyrics to every Bollywood song, but they've never lived through monsoon season. In my case, however, I've come to embrace the idea because, on a raw, primeval level, I am so confused. In a society obsessed with the concrete—identity and definition—I cannot even begin to uncover my roots.

i.

My first experience with that culture clash came in my elementary school years. In the early months of second grade, my father visits my class to give a presentation on Pakistan. The room brims with hushed excitement and antsy seven-year-olds, anxious to be entertained. Amongst the fidgeting fingers and tapping pencils, though, nobody's eagerness matches mine. Watching him walk into the classroom, I feel my chest rise into my head, like a buoy bobbing in the waves. I'm surprised my heartbeat doesn't drift right out of my ears and fill the air.

As he unwraps each foreign object, a roar of chatter erupts through the crowd. Girls giggle as he hangs my shalwar kameez up for all to see—sequins glimmering, reflecting across the windows and whiteboards. He plays music, shows dancing—the room overflows with thrill.

"That sounds Egyptian!"

"Those colors are so pretty!"

"That's such a funny outfit!"

Finally, he flips his PowerPoint to a slide of a map. With a red laser pointer, he outlines the borders of Pakistan, playing connect-the-dots with the topography that makes our country.

"When I was a young boy," he says, "we used to joke that on a map, Pakistan looks like a sitting dog."

And suddenly, sonorous laughter.

"A dog?!"

"That's so silly!"

"I think it looks more like an old lady!"

"I see it!"

"I don't . . . wait, now I do!"

To this day, I am ashamed to admit, in the midst of all that joy, I felt worthy. Respected. In the eyes of my peers, my culture finally meant something. Even in my own mind, I believed I understood my roots—as if the calls of my ancestors could be found in shimmering satin or Bollywood film.

But after that presentation, Pakistan was just a quaint fairy tale to my classmates—like a strange trip down the rabbit hole or Neverland. The way they gawked and gasped is no different than when men catcall me on the street, call me "exotic," ask me where I'm from.

"No, but where are you actually from? That sounds Egyptian!"

"I have such a thing for foreign girls. . . . That's such a funny outfit!"

"You're so hot for a brown girl. A dog?! That's so silly!"

My heritage is a commodity, a disposable good.

When those children trace the outline of Pakistan on an atlas, they don't see a nation. They don't see a civilization—a community of people.

They see a red laser pointer outlining an obedient dachshund, kneeling at the feet of its owner. They imagine sequins, Egyptian music—bright colors contrasting against white-walled classrooms.

The worst part is that so did I.

ii.

As the years went by, the legends and ideas that framed Pakistan in my mind were replaced by much harsher reality.

I remember the moments themselves very briefly, scattered like fractal patterns of a kaleidoscope.

Solemn expressions. A neatly packed suitcase.

Silence—the overwhelming kind, which rushes like a river. The kind you swim against, upstream, as if the absence of voices drowns you.

I remember numbers that I still cannot comprehend.

83-F. C-4. 26,000 feet per second. 120 pounds.

But despite all these little fragments of memories, I do not remember that day.

On March 11, 2008, my father's childhood home in Lahore, Pakistan, was demolished in a suicide bombing, desecrating the ancestral grounds of my people. The perpetrators were escaped militants, held and interrogated by the Punjab government in a Special Investigations Unit safe house behind our property. I recall these facts because they have been repeated time and time again, but I do not remember that day.

The jarring part, which I myself have yet to face, is that I know why I don't remember. I have tucked the memory deep inside my chest, letting it settle in the sickle-shaped cavity of my ribs, because I know exactly what I felt that day.

Nothing.

My family lost a piece of lineage deep in insurmountable rubble, and I felt nothing. I had lost nothing. I watched on like an outsider as ruins buried the myths that made my father. He gazed on as kitchen spices, baby cradles, summer nights in monsoon season—all fell to their knees. He saw hallowed ground, decades of laughter and birth, of death and mourning. I saw the back of a postcard, an image in a history textbook. In my mind, I could not distinguish those familial remains from Roman or Mughal forts—the centuries-old wreckage of long-gone empires.

The next day in school, I wear a pleated plaid jumper, and my frizzy, mangled hair plops down like a bird's nest atop my head. We learn Spanish, and the foreign words prickle—like fizzling candy on our tongues. We laugh at the gibberish sounds because we do not understand.

In Social Studies, our teacher flattens the whole world onto paper. Children stretch in their seats, pointing at the amorphous bumps of land and water, grasping at the picture-book colors. I join in, having forgotten all the grief of the day before.

"My dad told me Pakistan kinda looks like a sitting dog!"

"That's so silly!"

"I see it!"

"I don't . . . wait, now I do!"

Over the years, that nothingness has eaten away at me. The memory I buried inside resonates through my bones, gnawing at my lungs. I worry that if I were to go back to that picturesque, white-walled classroom and finally press my hands against that atlas, the whole world would cry out in pain.

Teaching Little Girls to Turn Into Plastic Dolls Inspired by Jamaica Kincaid

CARISSA CHEN, Grade 12, Age 17. Phillips Exeter Academy, Exeter, NH.
Matt Miller and Elizabeth Dean, *Educators*

I think, therefore I am
a man. Woman is free
but everywhere in chains;
let your gender shackle you
to the kitchen cabinet.

As your children grow up, feed the boy more, he needs it for his bones; feed the girl less, she must be pretty and skinny. As your children grow up, give the boy the books, the LEGOs, the swords. Give your daughter a doll; give your daughter a doll with ridiculous proportions; tell your daughter as you give her the doll that this beautiful, beautiful, sexy doll is a gift; do not think about the doll's mocking waistlines, platinum-blonde hair, plastic, plastic smiles. This, honey, is how you undress a doll, yank off the clothes forcefully; and darling, this is how you braid her hair; a repetitive weaving motion–in, out, in, out. Momma, why isn't my hair straight and blonde? Why can't I braid it?

Do not ask questions! Questions are for boys! Do not read, books are for boys! Here, take this toxic glitter eyeliner instead! Do not construct LEGO buildings, knowledge is for boys! Here, take this scratchy, itchy dress instead! Oh honey, do not speak, words, thoughts, and opinions are for boys! Here, take this fake Easy-Bake Oven and cook dinner instead!

Honey, come here and look at the mirror. Take your finger and pinch the skin covering your eyes. Trace your nails in a moon-shape semicircle, do you notice how the skin folds now? Look how much bigger your eyes seem! You don't look sleepy, bored, or Asian anymore! Honey, you really should try double eyelid surgery. The kids won't make fun of you on the school yard.

Oh darling! That much glitter eyeliner? People will think you're a slut just like you really are! Oh honey! That ugly dress? People will think you're fat just like you really are! Oh baby! That pink cupcake from your Easy-Bake? Don't you listen? You need to be pretty and skinny if you want to find a good husband.

Momma, I think I want to be a doctor! But all girls faint at the sight of blood! Oh now, stop crying, girls always cry too much! And then they ask why they can't be in business or science or law. Tears would spill over the dollar bills! They can't make money! Tears would ruin the DNA samples! They don't know how to control themselves! Tears would flood over their law cases! They don't know how to speak, let alone save themselves!

Come here, I'll teach you a trick: Mix rice wine with *mahlab* if your stomach swells, get rid of that baby girl. My grandmother taught me, mix an ounce of the wine, perhaps a dash of apple cider vinegar, and season with mahlab. Some call it gendercide: ten million Indian baby girls dead in ten years, 200 million baby girls aborted in China. Swallow all the liquid, let it lick the back of your throat,

over and over,

and now honey,

begin to clean the sink.

Snow

HAILEE COOK, Grade 12, Age 17. Arrowhead Park Early College High School, Las Cruces, NM. Tamara Miller-Dwake, *Educator*

Perhaps we meant in spring.
But who could remember?
Flowers grew from our pores
And we watered them for one another,
Though they became too invasive.
Then fall came around,
Painting the horizon in warm colors
To mask the death of its kiss
And a cold so bitter,
Like we'd become,
I instantly craved
The hundred-degree weathers of summer.
The frigid air kissed our lips softly,
Chilling us to the bone.

I still think of you in snowstorms.
I still see your ghost in my breath
That warms the air
As the pavement glistens,
Illuminated by a light I will never reach.
The snowmen we built never lasted,
Melting alongside us.
Each flake that hit the ground did too.
We're no longer glitter falling from the sky
Like in snow globes.
We're not frozen in a perfect moment.
But I still think of us as snow.

And when your birthday passes
I'm still left here to remember
Those freezing black nights
That saw the first flurry.
How icy white flakes
Would collect on your hood
While you'd stick out your tongue—
A desire for something,
Even if it meant you'd destroy it.
I see you running
And crashing
And red stains the snow of my dreams.
I see your smile lit in the moonlight
And mourn the secrets I still keep for you.
I see our abandoned hopes reflecting in the
Hot chocolate that reminds me of you
And leaves a forlorn taste in my mouth.
Maybe I'd move on
If I didn't feel myself falling,
Each year with you
And the snow.

Chacha's Pamilya

SETH GOZAR, Grade 12, Age 18. Douglas Anderson School of the Arts, Jacksonville, FL. Elizabeth Flaisig, *Educator*

When Chacha isn't standing on the street in her short shorts and tight tank and high heels, she's at Mercury Drug, digging through the makeup clearance buckets. She says makeup is a safer alternative to bleaching pills—more mestiza means more customers.

Chacha doesn't live here anymore, but she still services us. She moved back to her old house a while ago, but when Juban comes over, she crosses the street and pretends. She just leaves the house lights on and dusts off her old bed.

Sometimes she walks the dog and passes by once, twice, three times. Sometimes, she leaves the shit on our driveway.

Chacha lives so close, all we do is yell out the window. She comes because sometimes the men are too much to handle, she says. Every minute spent away from the street means another minute they'll grovel for more.

But we shouldn't have to wait so long for Juban to come home, Chacha said once, quietly. Shouldn't have to pretend because he loves us.

More quietly—he should love us.

We know this.

Chacha comes often—more than Juban. He's too busy betting on cockfights and buying *putas* to spend time at home. According to her, what Juban spends is enough to fix up our *bahay* and buy two more.

Juban likes to think we're a big happy family. We think that's silly, because he doesn't really live with us. When Juban comes over, Chacha shakes his hand, takes his coat, and fixes the spare bed they used to sleep in. But he never follows her. He sleeps on the couch in his nice suit, not long after handing her some cash, and maybe some yellowed palm crosses.

Still stupid, she says. Doesn't know a good puta when he sees one.

Before Juban left, he was the one Chacha took care of. We pretended when he'd bring her for dinner. There wasn't a dog then, so there wasn't any stale poop to scoop up. We vacuumed and swept and scrubbed so we could walk around the house without shoes on—people on TV do it a lot, Juban said, so it probably means something.

We cleaned out the oven and actually used it for *lechon* shoulder and *leche flan*—real food, not frozen servings.

We never saw them kiss, even though we wanted to.

They dated until Juban went on his first mission. Juban said the mission was his life now, so he and Chacha were done. There wasn't any fighting. Chacha moved back to her house, and Juban started visiting less and less.

Eventually we knew it was OK to talk to Chacha again. She started pretending with us because no one else would.

No one sleeps on their old bed because of what Chacha told us. When the breakup was still fresh, she said Juban enjoyed putas on that bed but never her. He touched her but couldn't feel.

Her dog doesn't care, but do dogs count as someone?

When we asked, Juban said no. He quoted something—dogs and other animals didn't have souls, so no. They made better meals than friends.

It was kind of mean, the way he said it, and Chacha agrees.

Don't listen to him, she laughs. If you ask tomorrow, he'll say yes. That man is too fickle. He'll jump around never knowing the best's already gone.

But you're still here.

Ai. She sighs, over thawed lasagna.

Galvanizer

ELIZABETH LEE, Grade 12, Age 18. Boise High School, Boise, ID.
Jennifer McClain, *Educator*

"Please, sir, all I want is some chestnuts."
The girl on the corner of Lester and 10th is thin;
her spindly legs weave shivers from the particulate chill.
She has been there since yesteryear, and all they do is look
through her until she's barely even there
She stretches out one pale sapling arm to brush the edge of a
thick wool coat
But the banker pulls it from her fingers and mutters a curse
at the icy street.
The banker is brisk, talks crisp like the crinkle of clean cash,
and never listens more than he can help
His ego is a black hole, never satisfied
destined to putrefy in the artificial heat of a warm hearth fire.
Raised on the fear of desperation, he devours falsehood to
forget, forges false security from failure
He snaps at his son to step lively, look alert
Whose boy is he? this slowpoke;
Not his, surely.

His son
wants faith, not finance;
friendship, not fame.
His son
forgets his mittens and runs back to Lester and 10th
digs into the bottom of his freshly pressed pants pocket and
folds a coin into her hand.
Not enough for chestnuts, but enough for amity;

Sometimes enough is more than enough.

Her eyes are champagne; lighter than sky,
rounder than rain—
"Would you like to hear a song?"

She sang the way hope sings,
because no one knows hope quite like those who clutch it between two empty hands
She sang the way the moa sang, when it found itself the only one of its number
She sang the way her mother sang, had she been old enough to remember
She sang her street corner, the rattling carts, the footsteps, the pain,
the people, the vendors, the shame
The days she huddled with the company of the words in her head, the song in her ear,
the beating of her heart that told her she had pluck

She is not proud to be poor;
She is proud to be unprecedented,
to pry at the insides of things and prove that people purport importance, not purpose,
preserve power, not peace
Her gift is authenticity, and the boy puts it in his pocket—
a present well-made for a price well-paid.

Perhaps with those chestnuts, she would have grown up brave and beautiful,
honey-sweet and happy to share her pennies.
But a heartened heart, she thought, is worth more than a hearty stomach
and oftentimes it is so.

A Good Heart

ALIXANDRA WILENS, Grade 12, Age 17. John F. Kennedy High School, Bellmore, NY. Vivian Lopez, *Educator*

Dragons have been forced to play the villains in stories since humanity could write. It has been their responsibility to ensure that there was always a village in peril, or a princess locked in a tower, so that knights could have a place in which to plunge their swords. They have obediently taken such a job to give humankind a goal worth striving toward. Just as there can be no light without darkness, there can be no hero without a villain. They serve their purpose well, courageously sacrificing their happiness, their own lives, to give humanity champions.

Why did they have to become the lions trapped in arenas to fight mortal gladiators in the first place? The most logical argument many gave was that the dragon had to be destroyed before it had the opportunity to burn down the kingdom. Still, what indication did any royal court ever receive that this would have been the dragon's intention? Did it send forth a proclamation claiming the kingdom's land as target practice? Did it press its footprint into the ground as a sign of marking its territory? No, it only had the ability to create fire, and therefore, as ancient men and women so naïvely believed, it must without a doubt have been guilty of wanting to burn down the realm. Some believed that since it had wings, it could fly up to the sun and cover it, forcing its supposed mortal enemy, the human race, into darkness. Did anyone suggest that the scales on its wings would create more light, not less? Of course not, who would dare to side with something not human, something Other? Nobody ever stopped to consider that a man is not executed for having the potential to kill another if all he does is pick up a knife; yet dragons said nothing.

Dragons have been charged with giving humans new battles to fight because they are Other, and everyone has, no matter how well hidden, some fear of Other. Dragons' powerful tails brand them as different. Their shining scales gleam against the sun, a perfect target. Their breath of fire streaks across the sky, leaving a trail of breadcrumbs no hunter can resist. Dragons have been burdened with leading brave warriors to dark caves, evil lairs, and tall towers, but, when handing out roles, no one ever asked them if they would rather have played the heroes themselves. Who is to say that they do not spend their lives wishing they could instead save strangers from the cold, light the path for those who have lost their way, and give comfort to those who are afraid of the dark? Perhaps they desire for a cheering crowd as they fly off into battle, and the promise of comfort and love to return to when they are trudging through the darkness. Nobody asked what their hopes and dreams were, instead assuming that sharp teeth meant they were looking for bodies to sink them into. Even as a little girl looks to the sky with longing, dragons look down upon the world with their secret desire: acceptance.

The oldest struggle in human history is the fight for tolerance. Must a dragon be evil because it is different? So many men and women wish they could have scales to protect themselves from the pain others inflict, but the truth is that dragons have worn such protection, and they would say that it makes little difference. The hatred still stings, still inflicts wounds the eye does not see but the soul never forgets. The most fatal.

The dragon is simply a creature that is pure of heart, that feels the sting of swords wherever it flies but still flies on, that knows that rancor is a weapon worse than any Excalibur, and that understands what it is like to be trapped in the sky. Dragons wish to be accepted, but there will always be knights who think that behind each dragon lies a blonde, blue-eyed princess, so they take the cards dealt to them in life with their heads held high. They know of their own genuine intentions, and they continue to be the heroes they wish the humans could see them as, while still playing the parts of the villains the world needs.

They blow just enough fire to light a traveler's way without revealing the outline of their shadow. They give just enough warmth to a poor family's cottage without setting fire to the roof. They provide a nightlight for the little boy too afraid of the dark to sleep, the child drifting away to the sound of rumbling breath he so easily mistakes for wind. The dragons can follow their passions to themselves without ignoring their duties to the world. As the gallant knight saunters away with her arm around her prince, the dragon smiles, flying away in covert triumph, the secret of its pure heart locked in the sky.

Jazz in the Park

CHASITY HALE, Grade 12, Age 18. Miami Arts Charter School, Miami, FL.
Jen Karetnick, *Educator*

A ritardando—
the music moves like a bronze coin,
spinning with every key stroke,
but now, it is caught in the asteroid belt
and slowing, scattered notes
starve the me that needs completion.

The music never really ends; it only widens.
Soon, it will be a dwarf planet,
the only one I want to hold,
finitely spitting its music into time-space.

Grandma is pulling my sweater sleeves now.
I hold her arm beneath the wristwatch.
We head for the coffee shop as she tells me,
on the lawn, we're like coyotes,
up to our ankles in Rocky Mountain dust,
howling, not at the moon, but at all of it—
every interstellar body, every cosmic wink
in the vacuum that swallowed our songs
the very instant they were launched
from the grand piano.

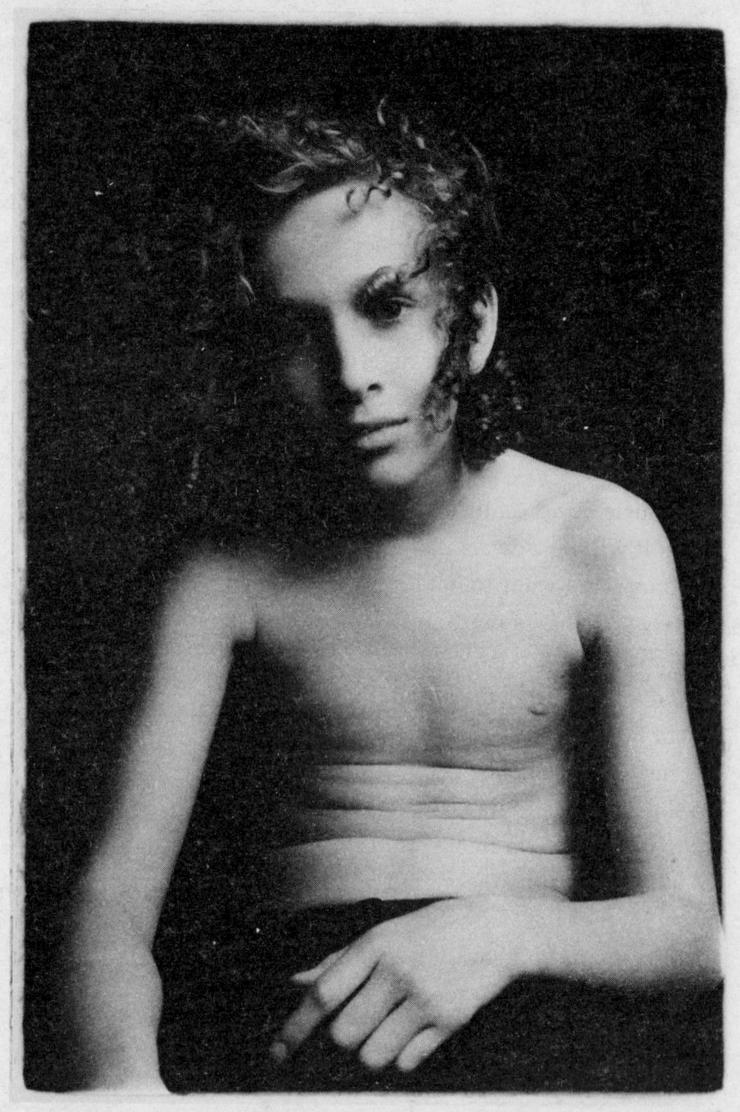

LEILA GRILLO, ***Jet***, Grade 11, Age 16, John Marshall High School, Los Angeles, CA. Michael Going, *Educator*

SPONSORED AWARDS

Dedicated and generous sponsors make it possible for us to provide additional recognition and scholarships. In 2017, we were pleased to add a new opportunity—the New York Life Award, sponsored by the New York Life Foundation. We were also grateful to continue the following Sponsored Awards: The Herblock Award for Editorial Cartoon; The RBC "Flaunt It" Award; the Gedenk Award for Tolerance; the Neiman Marcus Awards for Fashion and Jewelry; and the Best-in-Grade Awards, sponsored by Bloomberg Philanthropies.

American Voices Award

The American Voices Award is the highest regional honor and is presented to only one writer from each region. Works that most exemplify originality, technical skill, and the emergence of a personal voice receive this Award.

Selections of these awarded writing works are included in the following pages.

Some of the writing selections have been excerpted. Visit **artandwriting.org/galleries** to read all of the work as it was submitted.

To Look Like My Mother

CHRISTINA LEWIS, Grade 9, Age 15. Charleston County School of the Arts, North Charleston, SC. Danielle DeTiberus, Francis Hammes, and Beth Webb Hart, *Educators*; Gedenk Award for Tolerance

I remember your eyes like juniper
and mint leaves, the eyes you said held me
when I was just a twinkle
in your mind. Narrowing at the girl

who refused to sit on my bed
because I was too dark, and brown
paint stained. The first moment I remember
looking up at you,

your hair brushed like honey, curling
like the corks you collected from wine
bottles. Just long enough to shield my seven-year-old
face from the girls who whispered
behind their porcelain fingers, and your friends

who asked in the supermarket
if I came from a mission trip in Guatemala.
I looked up at your skin,
rosy from the camellias that blossomed under your cheeks.

Stretched over your bones and brushed the color
of rice my grandfather harvested with hands
like mine, fifteen thousand miles away from where we lived.
You were white in the places

it mattered. I wanted to take magic
marker to my irises and scribble ink that matched
pine needles and Atlantic sea foam, to twist

my hair like the bottle caps that swiveled onto and sealed
glass Coke bottles too expensive to buy
in India. I wanted to look like you and that girl, to snatch
the pale foundation from your bathroom counter

and rub it into the creases of my eyelids and the folds
of my knees that tanned too easily, never turning
cherry. I wanted to burn like you. Longed for the sun to
touch me, unafraid.

Omaha

HUDSON QUINN, Grade 7, Age 13. St. Stephen's Episcopal School, Austin, TX. Victoria Woodruff, *Educator*; Best-in-Grade Award

January 1944

We all took pamphlets of where we would be deployed. And that is when I met him.

"Hey, you were deployed to the same base that I was! Guess we're gonna be buddies, right?"

He was short, brown-haired, and blue-eyed. He looked like the kind of person who you could fall next to and expect to be caught.

"Yeah," I said, "I guess we are."

"My name's Alan. Alan Bow." He grinned with every syllable, in a way that seemed odd but comforting.

"Charlie Richards."

"Well, we are gonna have a great time being shot at."

"I can't wait."

February 1944

All I could think about was the cold. The mind-numbing, unbearable, and agonizing cold. We stood in line and shivered as the drill sergeant strolled up, comfortable as if it were a summer day.

* * *

In the middle of the sea of unfamiliar and stern faces, I spotted one that I knew. In fact, the very one that I was looking for. I hadn't noticed Alan at first, because he had been hidden by the other, much taller soldiers. I didn't greet him at first, fearing that the drill sergeant would punish me for it. But after we were dismissed to eat, I sat with him and talked about Brooklyn and other things. We chatted for quite a long time until we were called off and went to sleep.

I dreamt of home and my family. I wondered how they were doing without me. How could they get by? I didn't know. I hoped that somehow Frank and my mom could find work somewhere. I could only hope.

The next day, we lined up and I was standing next to Alan when I heard a whisper next to me. Well, it wasn't quite next to me. It was more a lot farther up. It was quite a bit taller than me. I turned and saw the most massive person I had ever seen. He had dark-brown skin and black eyes that seemed to pierce my soul.

"Hey, kid, what's your name?" he said in a deep voice.

"Ch-Charlie. Charlie Richards," I responded shakily.

"Well, Charlie . . . " He moved his hand and I flinched, expecting a fist. Instead his hand extended to me. "It's a pleasure to meet you."

"Uh . . . thanks."

"I'm Peter. I'll see you around."

We burst into formation as we heard the whistle, and we began the rigorous schedule that the drill sergeant had cut out for us.

Later that day, I was shoved from behind as I heard a snicker behind me. As I looked up I saw a man with a mean, savage face.

He radiated hatred and malice.

"Hey, kid," he sneered. "Why are you falling down? Got a problem, shorty?"

He laughed and made a rather rude gesture with one hand. He turned to walk away and I spat at his feet. He turned and raised his fist. I put my arms above my head and felt the impact once, twice, but the third did not come when I expected it to. Instead I heard a squeal and looked up as Peter held his fist in his hand as the man looked up in horror.

"Is there something wrong here?" Peter asked in a calm but firm voice.

"Uh . . . nothing at all. I was just . . . going."

"What's your name, big man?" he asked.

"J-Joseph," the man stuttered.

"You should probably leave."

Joseph ran off but glanced back at me in anger, a look of hatred in his eyes.

"Thanks a lot, Peter," I said in appreciation.

"Glad to help," he said, and then wandered off. It's nice to have friends in high places.

Late May 1944

Word flooded through the compound. After months of standing around in Allied territory, we were finally being deployed. My unit, which was composed mainly of the soldiers I had trained with, was one of many to be deployed on a beach of Normandy.

It was called Omaha. Omaha Beach.

I turned and faced Alan, who was deep in pensive thought. Later that night, I stared at the picture of my family and wondered if I was going to die.

Daughter Calls It "Done"

SUSANNAH PITTMAN, Grade 10, Age 15. Hastings High School,
Hastings-on-Hudson, NY. Ross Abrams and Robyn Royal, *Educators*;
Best-in-Grade Award

Daddy writes about numbers.
And Momma writes about feelings.
And Daughter don't write.
And together they wrote a poem.
And Daddy called it "Marriage."
And Momma called it "Love."
And Daughter called it nothing.
They read it to all their neighbors,
pulling back lips
to reveal rotted smiles.
And Daughter would bounce off the bus
with stacks of papers,
pretty A's painted across.
And Momma hung them up high on the fridge
branded with gold stars.
Not long after
cards flooded their mailbox,
filled with the types of things people say
when there's nothing to say at all.
And they also sent food
that singed her throat with pity,
until she much preferred the taste of hollow.

And now Daughter stumbles off the bus
with stacks of papers,

other letters stained across.
And Momma shoves them in a cardboard box
that's splitting at the seams.
Daddy wrote about numbers,
but he can't see them anymore.
And Momma wrote about feelings,
but she doesn't have them anymore.
And Daughter didn't write,
but now she braids chains of clauses
into sentences that chip away at the teeth they escape.
She bends her sentences into tercets
or couplets and even single lines.
And splices them into a poem.
And Daddy called it nothing.
And Momma called it fiction.
Daughter reads it to her classmates.

And finally
after hours spent stuffing scribble
down a marble notebook's gullet,
Daughter calls it "Done."

Melancholy

CIARA SING, Grade 11, Age 16. Pittsburgh CAPA School, Pittsburgh, PA.
Mara Cregan, *Educator*; Best-in-Grade Award

A black boy told me that he never met a black girl with an
afro that could pronounce every syllable in the word
ignorant, that he never met a black girl
who sleeps in satin scarves and dreams about gravitational
fields so intense no matter, no particle could ever escape,
almost as if he never met a black girl
who broke down his stereotypes. As if we should keep the
curves in our hips but not in our smile, as we allow the media
to desensitize our generation,
as intense hate gets injected into our system and tells black
girls to become apologetic for their race.
Black girls whose water is poisoned with lead, who become
numb to the taste of their own tongue. Black girls who are so
used to white wine intoxicating their thoughts,
sisterhood is no longer sensational.
He told me that he never met a black girl who's a black girl
and loves being a black girl. As if self-love doesn't come along
with the melanin, as if self-confidence
gets lost in our curls and respect gets left behind in the
swishing of our thighs. He told me that he never met a black
girl who doesn't believe she'll give birth
to a convict. He said he never met a black girl who doesn't
like being the Sarah Baartman spectacle, inspected and
experimented on, tagged as the unidentified
species. It seems like sometimes black boys forget their black
lips use to suck on black nipples.

My Elephant and Me

ALEXA RUSSELL, Grade 10, Age 15. Pryor High School, Pryor, OK.
Stephanie Bennett, *Educator*; New York Life Award

Months passed, and my loneliness consumed me. I cried silently most mornings, trying not to draw attention to my grief while desperately wishing for someone to notice. I walked to class with my elephant in tow, two tons of hurt weighing down on my soul. I wore elephant bracelets on my wrist as a physical acknowledgment of my sorrow. One day out of nowhere, a friend asked what they were for. I smiled, so grateful for that tiny spark of hope.

"They're for my brother. He has trisomy 13, and they don't think he'll live."

"Oh, I think I'll get one too."

One simple sentence, and suddenly a pet elephant didn't seem like such a difficult thing to have.

December was fast approaching, bringing my brother's due date with it. But it was only November, and I told myself I still had time with him. My elephant was getting antsy; breaking down became more common. It was the 10th when my dad picked me up from school. I got in the car and instantly felt the thick gloom in the air. He turned to me with fear and sadness in his eyes.

"It's time."

We got home and told my sisters that Mom was being induced. We'd get to meet our brother in the morning. They must have forgotten about the doctor's words, because they jumped and hollered without a care in the world. I stared at my mother's face, her uncertainty as clear as day.

"Please, no. Not yet."

I prayed. We were supposed to have a little while longer.

That evening I rode to the hospital with my parents as the family elephant dutifully followed the car. My sisters had stayed behind with our grandparents, who would bring them in the morning when the doctors were supposed to begin inducing. We waited in our room as nurses busied themselves around us. As the sun set, we laid down and slept on the rigid hospital couch. My elephant curled up in the corner. We would need our strength for the next day.

I was the last of the three of us to wake up that morning of November 11. I was about to get in the shower when my mom yelled for my dad.

"Get the nurse! Something just fell out!"

They ushered me out of the room and told me to wait with my aunt, who had just arrived. I left in my pajamas with greasy, unwashed hair and sat in a standard hospital chair. We waited until the nurse came and took me back to the room.

"They sent me to get her."

I walked in, more nervous than I had ever been in front of any other boy. That is until I saw his face. My parents had told us he wouldn't look the same as everybody else. My father handed me my brother, and I fell in love. It didn't matter that he had a cleft lip, that some things were a little different, because he was perfect, from his head to his eleven toes. As tears ran down my cheek, I stared, drinking in all I could of this precious baby in my arms.

"It's going to be OK."

My dad wrapped me in his arms as I handed my brother back to my mom. I continued to cry as I hugged my father. I had been so worried about that moment, and there I was. I felt truly alive with my love for my brother. Tears just kept coming. Despite how I appeared, I was finally at peace. All those months I had lived in fear, anxiously waiting for God to do something, and there my miracle was. In my arms, I held the beautiful baby brother God had promised.

It had been 9:03 a.m. when my brother literally fell into the world. We loved him every moment he was here. We took a million pictures to capture it all. We were so overwhelmingly at peace and filled with so much joy. It was practically a zoo, with all the elephants in the room. On the bed, on our laps, and in our hands, elephants anywhere an elephant could stand. It couldn't have been a more wonderful day. My sisters and I read books to our little brother. My mom changed his diaper. My dad prayed over his son.

Even as we laughed, our time with him was ticking away. His heart couldn't beat fast enough to keep pace with our excitement. His brain couldn't quite fathom our love. His lungs couldn't breathe in enough of this life. At 5:08 p.m., I watched as my brother took his last breath. I watched his skin lose the colors of life. I saw the blood rush to his head as he struggled to stay a bit longer. Four-point-seven ounces of perfection was ripped away from us far too soon.

That evening I left with my sisters and my grandparents. We went to my house, and I fell asleep in tears. The greatest day of my life had passed, leaving me with nothing but an elephant.

My now constant companion sat at the foot of the bed that

night, watched over me and cried with me. He'd claimed me as his that day, and now he would never leave. He patted me with his trunk, laid himself down, and drifted off to sleep.

I remember the haziness of the next few weeks. We sat at home as people brought us food. Life wasn't as vivid as the day my brother was born. I floated in and out of reality, escaping the feeling of time. Our emotions were so raw, seeping onto our faces with every little change. One moment tears would flow abundant, only to be stifled by laughter in the next. Joy was so seldom that each little joke was savored for minutes on end. I remember my dad's face as such happiness crept over him. The pain so clear, yet the need to smile overcame it. His demeanor would change as he threw back his shoulders and tears welled up in his eyes, the purest kind of joy blooming amidst our sorrow.

My sisters returned to school rather quickly, but I stayed behind. Their classmates sent us cards, and knew what was happening. On the other hand, I knew all that I would receive was blank stares and hard questions about my two-ton friend. My elephant wasn't ready for such rejection and disregard. No way could I expose him when we both had healing scars.

For the next couple of weeks, I avoided school in favor of my elephant. He had taken it upon himself to never leave my side. Sometimes he stretched himself across my chest, crushing my heart without any warning. I don't think he meant me any harm; he seemed oblivious to his own size. Thanksgiving came and went without a brother for me to thank. My family and I clung to each other in the small confines of our living room. Eating and sleeping became our only reason to move.

I finally returned to school after Thanksgiving had passed. I made myself invisible, avoiding the obvious questions of my whereabouts. I tried to keep my composure, shushed my elephant when he trumpeted in the halls. I walked into the art room and made my way around the class to the shelf with our projects on it. As my teacher handed me my sculpture, she asked the question I'd been bracing for.

"Is he still with us?"

I sucked in a breath, unable to form many words. I shook my head no.

"He was here for eight hours and five minutes."

I could feel her compassion as tears formed in her eyes, and she wrapped me up in a hug. There's no doubt that she was thinking of her son-to-come. My elephant watched as the scene played out, savoring the attention. I sat back down with a little bit of hope in my soul. It's amazing how much a single person caring lightens the load.

I went about my day, ignoring the trumpet calls of my invisible friend. I walked into the math classroom, and there my best friend stood, the only other one who knew what animal followed me around. She opened her arms when she saw me.

"Come here."

That's all she said. She didn't ask any questions. She was simply there with love in her arms. My second spark of hope that day. My elephant was practically bouncing off the walls with all the thoughts coming his way. I can guarantee you've never seen anything quite like that, the most massive creature jumping around. It only lasted a little while, then he settled down. He sat next to my desk the rest of the day, begging for attention that I didn't have to spare.

School went on like that, a circus of hide-and-seek with an elephant. He tried making scenes in the middle of class, but his two-ton temper tantrums went unnoticed by my peers. He'd sulk in my lap, not leaving room for much else. My life was consumed by an elephant, and I wasn't given any choice in the matter. Grief had interrupted my plans and wreaked havoc on my emotions. My brother was dead, and no one knew he had even lived.

Finally, ninth grade came to an end. I left the halls of the junior high along with the isolation that inhabited my days there. I thought the worst of it was over, but summer brought new challenges with it. My family flew across the globe to the beautiful little island of Oahu. There we explored new landscapes and terrains, but no matter where we went, a certain elephant couldn't be shaken. Grief still hung in the air. We were there for a reason, and the day was fast approaching.

***

"Did you know his name means 'ocean' in Hawaiian?"

Oh, Lanikai, "beautiful ocean," the shore where my heart now rests. The waves crashing on the beach. Perfect weather. A light breeze. June 24 my family walked along a white sand beach, all of us together, his ashes in tow. The sun hadn't risen. We were all alone. We walked until we came to a cove, a single tree jutting out into the water. I had already shed many tears as we watched the sun creep from under the sea. I drew my brother's name in the sand as the others scattered flowers all around. My dad drew a heart and placed what remained of ours inside. We sat together holding hands, an elephant watching right beside us. Then the wave came and swept my brother away.

"The wind and the waves still know his name . . . "

That song played in the background as my heart continued to break. I thought the worst of the pain had come at 5:08 p.m. on November 11, 2015, but I was wrong. The pain came in knowing it'd be a lifetime before I saw my brother's face again. For now, I'd have to live for what he left behind, a family, a legacy of love.

Summer Rain

ALYSON DEL PINO, Grade 12, Age 17. New World School of the Arts, Miami, FL. Christian Losa, *Educator*; American Voices Award

May

To the part of me that is trying to die:
Die.
Come out of my mouth and
Into my bathroom sink.
Let me wipe you from the edges of my
Lips in disgust and
Rinse you from my teeth with cold water
(I am in need of cold water).

June

My white friend tells me that I am not Caribbean.
I stick to a lawn chair at midnight as an ocean of a backyard glows a dull orange, illuminated by a nearby streetlight. I hold my phone in one hand and trace my caramel knees with the other over and over and feel sweat roll down my neck as the heat of the day lifts itself from the ground.
He stands his ground. "You're not Caribbean because you're not black. I read once that Cuba is so isolated in its political situation that it really has nothing to do with Caribbean culture, so you aren't Caribbean."
My stomach joins the heat in its upheaval. Streams of streetlight orange and red gurgle and churn in my throat and a million words make it to my heavy tongue but no further. My eyes like black rapids throb and sting and a bead of sweat catches at my collarbone as hundreds of people and places

from the island I'm from bubble and foam at my teeth.
"I have to go," I manage.
Summer is hotter than it's ever been.
***
In a dream,
A conquistador takes the machete with which
He slices tropical jungle and
Holds it against my back.

In a dream,
I ask the sun how it felt to come to fruition.
The sun wields no weapon but neither does she speak,
Only listens and burns and points to my skin,
showing me all of my predecessors, one by one,
And the ways in which she burned them too.

I have been listening and burning.
I have been listening and burning.

September
The part of me that was trying to die,
the part that remembers,
that holds and swims and writes in
run-ons like the poets of my island,
is trying not to die,
but to survive.
It is trying to wipe the pain from my chest;
to rinse my mouth and my lips
and the curve of my hips
with the water of a history that speaks only in survival:
Survive the men who claimed you in the name of god and
glory;

Survive the fields of sugarcane they erected to suck gold from your veins;
Survive the fear that grows like ivy in living rooms;
Survive, Survive, Survive

The part of me that was trying to die
Is trying not to die
But to come out of my mouth
In a language that has not forgotten me,
that speaks in rhythm, in rivers and tides
"I am both white sand and dark rock"
Yo soy la arena blanca y la piedra negra
"Yes, I am Caribbean"
Yo sí soy caribeña
Yo sí soy caribeña
Yo soy caribeña

The part of me that was trying to die
is trying not to Die,
but to Live,
Y tiene todo el derecho.

Fox, Transformed

KATHERINE LIU, Grade 12, Age 17. Adlai E. Stevenson High School, Lincolnshire, IL. Denise Foster, *Educator*; American Voices Award

I unhinged my jaw and it filled with rain. Water lapped
up my rim, flooded the cathedrals of my heart. Inside,
pearls corkscrewing in their chambers. Each a past
kiss, a kiss passed. From his to mine. My bloodstream
swollen with unplumbed mines. Your barbed wit pressed
to mine. So I'll throw your mountain. I'll hold a feast.
Every goblet clinks with wine, every nosing sticks
your jaded heart. I coughed and a flock of birds flew out.
Arrowed demise. Fortunes and hypnosis, I'll bludgeon
the barge. I had dreams to sluice the fever out of fruit.
Next comes redemption. Next comes disease. Ill at ease,
I'll stutter every quest. I'll give up your requests, and
never honor the righteous, or whitest of lies. Who gave
me morality? Who made me wax and wane? I swallowed
the rain and listened to where it lay, washing up again
against my throat. Steps through my bones. I watched
the birds peck and flock, fluted in the rain. I watched
them molt and die again. They turned back to my mouth.

The Blind Old Hag

SAGE ROBINSON, Grade 10, Age 16. Central High School, Rapid City, SD.
Kerri Severson-Stover, *Educator*; American Voices Award

It wasn't denial at all.
She was inundated with unabridged incredulity.
She was completely incapable of belief.
My tears were mirthless,
my truths were not juvenile fabrications.
I can't victimize a victim
or criminalize a criminal;
the reality is already tethered to the earth.
I am not at fault for her blindness.
But yet,
I had become the adversary,
and the devil
was still perceived as the holy angel
who could commit no wrongdoing.

When a Black Girl Gives Birth

TAYLOR CRAYTON, Grade 12, Age 17. Lusher Charter School, New Orleans, LA. Brad Richard, *Educator*; American Voices Award

1.
her body becomes hollow
  she loses the tang from her tongue
she bathes in lavender and grows thickened skin on her feet
  her thighs   worshipped stardust   attracts the attention of cold palms
her lover pops her bubblegum lip   she learns that lips are the fastest healing body part
  she fasts for three days   soaks her hair in coconut oil   bends pages of the holy book
ignores his love taps against her forehead   her forearm her cheek   her wrist
she buys BB cream to cover up the bruises growing like pansies from her throat

2.
her daughter
mixes bleach with her bathwater and scrubs her elbows with cut up lemons
because her father taught her   *ain't no man wanna marry a field nigga*
her skin blackens under sunlight   melaninated
black was never the new black   until a white girl tries her on as a costume
  she picks at perm scabs how black women pick out coffins for their unborn sons

a flood starts running down her legs
she culls at her roots how Eve pulled the fruit
she washes her face with chloride and cries

3.

her lover leaves her with butterfingers
she can't catch love taps anymore blood drips on tile floor
don't worry baby baby i'm sorry you can still be my Black African Princess
means i'll love you since no one else will
she bends at the nape in search for God
she listens to Lauryn Hill baptizes her son under banal prayers
she dreams of stapling her lover's palm to cross
and burning his ear with vodka
she writes a poem *Black Girl Disneyland* but her mother tells her that it doesn't exist

Hands Off My Identity: Dealing With Difference in a Diversifying Community

LINDSAY PIERCE, Grade 11, Age 16. Maret School, Washington, D.C.
Leesa Fenderson and Mason Henderson, *Educators*; The RBC "Flaunt It" Award

"Wow, your hair is so weird! Elliot, feel this!"

Though I did not know what it was at the time, I first experienced what can be called a microaggression on my first day at the Maret School, where I am currently in eleventh grade. I was a sixth-grader at the time, and I was extremely nervous; I spent half an hour picking out my outfit that morning. Maret is an extremely exclusive, affluent school in the middle of an even more exclusive, affluent neighborhood. It was not a place in which tall, athletic black girls were abundant. Nevertheless, there I was, having survived the excruciating application process to claim my spot in those halls. The actual logistics of the day have by now fled my memory, but one thing that stuck was our first break period. A series of couches were lined up in a hallway across from an array of bagels and hot chocolate, and the entire sixth-grade class was freed to mingle for fifteen minutes. I was talking to a girl I had just met, likely about soccer or classes or something equally casual. Suddenly, I felt strange hands on my head, specifically, on my hair.

At least ten different people (though the number is likely higher if you count stares and whispers) proceeded to pick apart my carefully constructed bun (or "poof," as they called it).

"Wow, it's so thick!"

"What do you do with it?"

"But how does it work?"

Bear in mind that this was my first experience with the majority of my classmates, and while there is something to be said for youthful curiosity, children are taught on their first day of preschool to respect others' personal space. I was extremely uncomfortable, and I wondered whether I had any right or reason to stop them, eventually electing to simply smile. I did not immediately tell a teacher, nor my parents, nor my siblings about that odd break period, though I'm not sure why. Several weeks later, I casually mentioned it at the dinner table.

Until I saw my mother's shocked, horrified face, I don't think I realized that something had really gone wrong. Though it had bothered me in the moment, no one in my class thought it odd, so I'd convinced myself it was just nervousness and continued about my business. People had continued to touch my hair; I had continued to smile and nod uncomfortably, continued to question whether I had a valid reason to refuse them. But with my mother's demands that I refuse anyone who tried touching my hair again came a troubling realization: I was essentially the only black girl in my grade. There were two or three girls with one black parent, but their mixed heritage had given them straighter, silkier locks in place of the coarse, puffy coils I continue to do battle with. There were black boys with hair the same texture as mine, but their hair was cut short, and several of them had grown up with the class and were no longer considered new objects of interest. I was seeing Maret in a new light, and the angle was anything but flattering. With my ever-fascinating curls now physically out of reach, students instead asked me pointed questions in the hallway. Several girls recoiled in shock when I revealed that I wash my hair every two weeks or so (my hair dries out easily, so washing often weakens the strands). Incidents like this wounded me, shaking my confidence in my choice of school. Because of hair, of all things. It seemed so silly, but those wounds, and more like them, haunted me all the way to high school. They still bother me today.

But was it really just about hair? *Psychology Today* has defined microaggressions as "everyday verbal, nonverbal, and environmental slights, snubs, or insults, whether intentional or unintentional, which communicate hostile, derogatory, or negative messages to target persons based solely upon their marginalized group membership" (Sue). Essentially, any action or reaction that negatively targets a marginalized group is a microaggression. Unfortunately, neither in that definition nor any other article did I find the answers to my classmates' questions: What if it was just a joke? What if it's true? What if the person or group being targeted is just overreacting? In my case, my classmates were curious; I was there, it was just hair after all. No one meant any harm. In this is the crux of the issue, the "whether intentional or unintentional" part that people often ignore. For me, and for many minorities, it is not about the intention or size of the action, but the effect of otherness it imposes. My classmates did not touch my hair because they had seen it before or to appreciate it; they messed up my bun because to them it was a foreign object, and by that logic they concluded that it was their right to investigate without permission. Microaggressions are at best uncomfortable and intrusive; at worst they can be traumatizing and alienating, as my experience almost became. For my classmates, this concept was difficult to comprehend.

One of my best friends (both then and now), and one of the first to unceremoniously grab my bun, was also the first to question my discomfort.

"Why do you always grab my hair?"

"Because it's poofy," she giggled, "and it's cool. It's kind of a compliment, actually. No one means anything by it."

A compliment: This is how many microaggressions are dismissed or explained away. As a black girl in America, I've had my fair share of these.

Tracks

LYDIA SHAW, Grade 11, Age 17. Friends Select School, Philadelphia, PA.
Suzanne Morrison, *Educator*; American Voices Award

We walked the train tracks nearly every evening, like clockwork . . . until one of us remembered a test they had the next day, or we got creeped out by the darkness and the shadows and sounds it brought, or our soles would start hurting, and we'd turn around and walk back the way we came.

We avoided the tracks themselves, of course, because of their electric charge. One of Danny's friends said he heard about someone our age who had stepped on the tracks once, and he was dead within a minute. His eyes were so big, the kid said, that they nearly popped out of his head, and his breathing sounded like a smoker's. He wheezed in and out, in and out, his chest heaving shakily, his hands groping up for something that wasn't there. Maybe it was for the stars, I remember thinking. Maybe we're all reaching up for the things we can't grasp. I proposed that theory to the twins during one of our walks.

"Oh, kid," Biscuit said, shaking his head. I was a month older than him and Danny, but they seemed like my big brothers anyway. "You're gonna get lost in that big ol' brain of yours."

The night we walked, the sun was setting in this beautiful

sort of way, a blend of pinks and oranges and blues and purples and all sorts of other colors that I can't describe. It was warm and humid, humid not in the way that catches in your throat but in the way that dances up and down the hair on your arm. I remember Biscuit was sneezing a lot—he had these ridiculous spring allergies that kept his nose tingling. Danny had an earbud in one ear, the other hanging down, which was a hip look, according to him, although only one ear got to hear music. The other got to hear Biscuit's sneezing and my footsteps.

It was Danny who cut through the seams of the quiet first. "Biz, if you don't stop sneezing, I'm gonna pull out some weeds and wrap 'em around your nose."

And I laughed, and Biscuit sneezed again and lightly punched his brother. "You better not," Biscuit said, "else I'll sneeze in your mouth."

That was how the game began. We went from one threat to another, gradually getting more ridiculous and weird, our laughs growing louder as the sun set.

It started getting dark soon after, but nobody mentioned wanting to turn back, and my legs were moving on their own now. I had a feeling that even if I wanted to tell them to stop, they would keep walking all around the world. So I didn't tell them to stop—neither my legs nor the twins. And we kept walking.

Here's the thing about consistencies: you never expect them to change. They're comfortable and stable, something that you think you'll have forever. You don't even begin to imagine what life would be beyond them, because life right now is immersed in them. And when you do imagine those things, a world of the unknown opens up: adrenaline mixed with fear, shaking hands, and worried smiles. The unknown is like the night sky—so filled with things you can't yet reach for, things that can seem overwhelming and yet so beautiful. Things that shine and strike wonder into the hearts of those who feel nothing. The dark that is still penetrable by a light that is small to us when it is far away, but huge and imposing up close.

Enter another consistency: We were always daring each other to do stupid things. One day I walked around the tracks without shoes or socks on, and that was just the least of the dares' intensities. We took them very seriously. And that night's dare brought an inconsistency.

"I dare you to throw a rock at the next train."

"Um, what? Do you know how dangerous that is?"

Then Danny's words opposing mine, teasing, mischievous, as always: "You scared, kid?"

Then Biscuit's: "I'll do it, and we'll be fine, and you'll see."

And probably more words were said but I can't remember them because I was laughing. I couldn't help it—I laughed whenever I was nervous, especially when things weren't funny at all.

I said, "Please tell me you're not going to hit the train."

***

"You can leave if it makes you uncomfortable," Danny told me. "We won't hold it against you."

My feet backed me up, tripping over Biz's. They're going to be fine, I told myself. I watched it go, and I watched Biz's arm rise and fall. I watched the unlucky thrown rock enter the train's orbit, and watched everything start falling. The noise was louder than anything before—piercing sounds of metal on metal and screaming that pricked holes in me and ran right through. Fire flowed over trees and train cars, a river that left only death in its wake. There was smoke, grabbing at my lungs with fist over fist. It danced on my arms in a belligerent fury, making the humidity from earlier seem only a soft ballet from my most distant dreams.

Ammagaru

SARAH BALDINO, Grade 11, Age 17. Sidwell Friends Upper School, Washington, D.C. Jennifer Solomon, *Educator*; American Voices Award

Mother, this here is a collection of my memories. They are windows in the hallway of my recollection, and I cling to them with care. Perhaps they will help you recall who you once were, and who you became. Perhaps you will remember what you gained and lost. Perhaps you will remember what is real and what is not. Perhaps you will remember me.

This window here is etched with silver lace, glinting in the sunlight, brushed with diamond dust. Through it I see a winding pathway shrouded in the colors I remember, flowers of red, yellow, and purple. A woman stands at the trail's end. Her feet are rooted in the blond sand, thick like a rug. As her fingers comb through her curtain of curls, she watches her children play with the setting Narsapur sun. She scans the horizon as if readjusting to a wide-angled lens. She is awaiting her husband's return from the night school. This, Mother, is my earliest recollection of you.

This one here is cloaked in stiff cotton drapes, crisp bars of white and blue running to the fabric's end. I can see us sitting on our sandstone patio, your regal frame delicately grooming my infested head, now drenched in coconut oil and camphor. You pass a fine comb through my greased locks, locating and promptly squashing every louse or nit that dares to meet the comb's steel teeth.

"Chinny, did you tell Raji?" you say.

"Yes, Ma."

"And?"

I avert my eyes. I can hear a bulbul calling to her partner. Her trills are lost as the wind rattles the mango trees in our orchard. A katydid scuttles around your left foot.

I could have told you how Rajiacca called me "Skeleton." I could have told you how she pocketed my gold chain. And I could have told you how she made me a pariah, the school untouchable. It wouldn't have mattered. You already knew who she was and what she did—you didn't care. Raji was your favorite. She was stunning—the envy of every mother, the aspiration for every girl, and the recipient of every boy's affections. She was your crowning jewel; your most prized possession. And nothing that I could say would detract from your adoration of your firstborn. She made you happy.

Next is a bay window. I've framed it in the jeweled tones that have always complemented your complexion. Here I see an armoire neatly organized with your treasures: colorful saris, gold coins, and stacks of rupees. I see you standing in front of the almirah, the "steel cabinet," as we'd call it. You had kept the books; you managed the finances. You were thorough and methodical. You saved money, made prudent choices, kept meticulous records—and took pride in it. I see a different look on your face, a softer smile. With all of your children out of the nest, pursuing degrees of higher education, you have come into your own. You are also older, now, Mother. But you've transitioned effortlessly. You are happy.

This window is bare; its only embellishments are the Egyptian cotton drapes that have been bleached by the sun's glare. Through the glass pane, I can see the arid roadway that skirted our property. A scuffed taxi sits parked beyond the gate, meeting the curb at a thirty-degree angle. Its driver, who is, without doubt, lacking a license, stands pridefully by his vehicle, his dark and lanky frame supported by the passenger door. I see myself lingering outside of our home, suitcases stacked by my side. You stand before me with face marred by the lines of worry etched into your brow. You step forward and hold my temples in both of your hands.

"Chinny—be safe," you say.

"I will, Ma—"

"You don't need to go. We have master's degrees here too. Raji did it t—"

"Ma," I say with a shake of my head. You clasp our hands together and bring the back of my palm up to your lips.

"Return soon," you breathe, guiding our entwined hands to your breast, hovering above your heart. With three shakes, you release my hands. They fall to my sides, slackened. The skin between my fingers clings together, cemented by the humidity of the midday Narsapur sun. Before stepping away from me with an empty nod, you baptise my forehead with a viscid kiss.

And when you snap, the driver scrambles to load my luggage into the trunk of his canary-yellow taxi. We stand together for a moment. My eyes are closed. I can smell the punch of dried ocean water mixing with the wind, which rustles the neem tree's spreading branches.

The driver clears his throat and makes his way to the backseat door, swinging it open with a grandiose bow, averting his eyes with misplaced respect. As he holds the door, I hitch my sari above my ankles and return my gaze to you. Your eyes are downcast, and your hands are folded. When the engine squeaks to life, you turn and retreat into the house, your slender wrists wrapped around your elbows in a hunched embrace. You are lonely.

I haven't decorated this window, and I'm not sure I ever will. Perhaps I'm not sure of the colors and textures to use. Might I want to match it with the mood? Might I want to retouch it? I need to look deeper now. I see you on my wedding day. You were a beacon in a pink silk sari, surrounded by a swarm of stiff cocktail dresses with pneumatic sleeves and pinstriped three-piece suits. I could tell that you were overwhelmed by my American wedding. But the truth is, Mother, that day I felt something different. When I take your hands in mine, I can sense that your grip has changed since the last time you let me go. Perhaps I had done something wrong. Perhaps you thought I had outgrown you across the miles we spent apart; you in India, and I in America. Perhaps I could've told you that I hadn't replaced you with a white man and a picket fence, a *sukha jeevatham*. But those words remained unsaid, hanging in the air, stagnant. At the reception you sit slack-jawed; with downcast eyes and hands folded neatly in your lap. You didn't even give Raji, now Mrs. Suhasini Patel, a second glance when she left with some dark-skinned man, their fingers laced together. Instead, you remained at your table and your *poha idli* remained untouched. You are distant.

Five Cigarettes I'll Probably Buy Again

JAMISON RANKIN, Grade 12, Age 17. Goose Creek High School, Goose Creek, SC. Nick Geary, *Educator*; Best-in-Grade Award

1. marlboro menthol

The very first cigarette you wedged between your teeth was one from your father's pack. You were twelve then, gazing at the gradual plume of smoke that pushed from his nostrils. The cigarette was always in his hand, just like the man before him —the man who burst his liver with Smirnoff before you were conceived. There were glass ashtrays scattered all across your relatives' houses. In the earlier days, maybe when you were four or five, the adults of your family spent nights in the dining room. Spent it circled all around a Scrabble board, the light overhead illuminating a haze of cigarette smoke. You watched from the doorway, eyes the shape of saucers, still spinning the wheels of a toy truck.

You can hear him telling your uncle how he smoked a pack down the day you were born and your mother's blood pressure rose and rose and rose—or maybe it was the day your brother was born, you can't remember—and he treated the cigarette as maybe something that calmed, maybe something that added to the turbulence.

You stole that cigarette from his pack while he slept through the morning, probably from working the late shift, you don't remember. And then, as you cut into the scrub woodland behind your neighborhood, you swore that you felt him watching when you held that black Bic up, your hands shaking. You sat by the creek, gentle water sifting through rocks and leaves, trying to enjoy it for what it was, trying to figure out what it was about a menthol cigarette that made everything better.

You could feel the reel of your father's disappointment scorching through your skin, burning your muscle to char, blackening the calcium of your bones. You didn't know how to inhale that cigarette. You let the heavy smoke sit in your mouth—that's what your father would be disappointed about the most. You figured out how to inhale it when you neared the filter, and your baby lungs damn near dropped out of your diaphragm.

Your father tells you he started smoking when he was twelve too, but your mother says he started younger. You know he coughs tar into the sink every morning, you know his arteries are thickening, you know he's the prime contributor to the drab of dark nicotine staining the household. And you know that you're no better than him, slowly thinning out his packs as you walk the dog and smoke down the street. Not even three weeks out of the hospital and he wanted to scrub the smell—the dark-yellow hue—from the walls. You helped him. Thirty minutes in, he leaned back from the gray-watered bucket and said he needed to take a break. He took the ashtray with him outside, a box of Marlboros poking out from his shirt pocket.

3. black and mild: wood tip wine

When you started driving your father's work car, it was the wrappers of the individual cigars that quickly made him catch on. You stuffed them in your pockets, but they fell out, and you didn't bother to think of checking. At first, you blamed it on the friend who never carried a pack, the friend who never smoked one—but carried around a little vaporizer like he used to. But he knew. Your father, shucking oysters in the fluorescent beam of the garage, his rough hands gliding the knife through the rocky shell, doesn't look up when he asks you.

He asks you how many you smoke a day. He asks it casually, almost as if he's interested, and this is when he turns to you. He doesn't look at you like he used to—he looks like he's known all along. Maybe he's been waiting for you to tell him. You can't lie this time, and you tell him the truth. He shrugs his shoulders and tells you to clean the wrappers out of the car. He goes back to shucking oysters.

You'll share lighters with your parents. The only time they yell is if you forget to give them back. There's a grocery list in the kitchen every weekend, and at the top, your mother's writing adds "cigarettes for him and her." You learn that if you add your name to that list, he'll come back with bread and eggs and a bag full of cigarettes. At the bottom of that bag, you'll find your Black & Milds, still in untouched packaging, waiting for your prying fingers.

5. the skyline cigarette

It's Marlboro. Not as heavy as your father's, not as mellow as the girl's. The menthol is enough to cut your tongue, but it's light, almost tasting of spearmint. But when you're in the shower and you start to cough, you hear the nicotine's edge against your sternum. You think of your father: the way he sounds when his lungs might unhinge, the way his breath pulses against his trachea. Maybe you'll sound like him when you're older. Maybe he expected this from you all along.

Several months have passed. The girl is waiting on the other end of the phone for you every night now, said she would rather have the 200 miles instead of nothing at all. You count down the days with her until you come home again, you feel right and ripe and somehow peachy and everything's back to normal when she's around. She hopes you write well. She hopes it's worth it. She hopes you aren't smoking in the dorm bathroom and blowing the exhale into the vent.

You'd smoked the Skylines before with a friend at a school yard, in a recess field both of you played in years ago. The monkey bars had begun to chip with paint, the rock-climbing wall scrawled with immature obscenities and misspelled cuss words. At the gate, the fence of the recess field was covered with jackets and lunch boxes kids had left behind. You stole a juice pack from one of those lunch boxes when your throat started to ache.

Now you smoke them on a ledge at a newspaper house, listening to the cars whir by below and the people walking the streets. You're careful with which way the wind blows—you can't let the nicotine cling to your clothes, you'll scrub your hands twice before you get back to campus. Your father let you go. He gives you a hard time for smoking now, tells you to kick the bad habit everyone else in the family has because you're better than that. He tells you that every time you light one up, it makes him want to smoke until he can't feel his throat, and you shrug your shoulders, light up again. You can just hear him, in his own head, saying, all these things I've done for you, and you're still like the rest of us.

The Llovenia Effect

MAKIYAH HARRIS, Grade 8, Age 13. R. B. Chamberlin Middle School, Twinsburg, OH. Melissa Walters, *Educator*; Best-in-Grade Award

The Llovenian sun is at its peak, the harsh red rays glaring down from the sky and onto the small black flower growing at the top of the hill. The clouds are painted shades of pink: blush, rose, magenta, the many hues giving life to a place that only seems to produce the opposite. The flower itself, however, is not as fortunate as the beautiful world above, contained in layers and layers of a transparent atmosphere, dotted only by the blush-rose-magenta puffs sprinkled upon it like thin films of dust suspended in air. No. The flower is darker, lonelier, uglier. A sharp contrast to the benevolent sun that keeps watch from miles away. And yet, somehow, that tiny shriveled crust of a plant, a dark twisted thing, holds more truth about the nature of this planet than every star in the sky, every scarlet ray bearing sun, every voluminous poof of gas. This flower alone knows more about this planet, the supposed promised land of Llovenia, than the entire galaxy. Because it is there, rooted firmly to the surface, a witness to every cruelty, every injustice. The small flower, whose leaves are now crumbling to sand and whose petals are turning to paper, knows that Llovenia is evil. The bud cries out to the occasional passerby, shrieking for them to take care, to practice caution. Its voice is often left unheard, for all of those who hear it choose to listen too late. Days too late, weeks too late, months too late. I am one of these travelers. I am days-weeks-months too late. And now I am lost.

You might not think me to be one to talk to plants, much less agree with them, but then again, Llovenia has a way of luring things out of people that even they were never aware of. Silent monsters. Invisible monsters. Deadly monsters. I suppose my silent-invisible-deadly monster is insanity. Yes, this monster has endless rows of razor-sharp teeth, teeth that are so stiff that you don't even hear them as they comb the air, searching for a meal to snatch into its jaws. Soundless. Teeth that are so pointed, so sharpened that you don't even feel them when they slice into you as easily as a knife through butter. Painless. Teeth so quick, so final, so thorough that you don't even notice you've died until you are nothing more than a sad, lost soul. Daystoolateweekstoolatemonthstoolate.

***

Her pale face is illuminated by the simple white light above us, shadows hitting it at an angle that emphasizes the sharp curve of her cheekbones and large red eyes as scarlet as her planet's sky. A violet lock of hair has fallen from her complicated arrangement of braids and plaits, resting over a thin eyebrow. New Face smiles at me. I bite my lip. "Hello, Leya." New Face speaks softly, as if she's scared she'll break me by screaming.

Humph, I snort, thinking of the voices. Well, it's a little late for that, now isn't it? The voices in question chuckle at the irony, filling my head with deep cackles. New Face cocks her head as the voices convince me to laugh too. She whips out a flat little circle and a glowing orange stick, writing something in a language I can't understand. "Hello, Leya," New Face repeated herself over my hysteric giggles, "My name is Andara."

Andara? There's no section for Andaras in my archive of people. I make one, filing her and her round pad thing under it. I glance up at her, now quiet. She looks relieved. "Leya, do you know how long you've been here?"

How long have I been here? How long? Too long? Too late? Daystoolateweekstoolatemonthstoolate. The black flower warned me. It knew I would be late. Too late. Toolatetoolate toolate. I pause my rapidly flowing thoughts just enough to catch the Andara's concerned look, furrowed brows knitting together as she grabs her writing circle again. Had I been muttering out loud? Had she seen my silent-invisible-deadly monster lurking in the shadows? Idontknowidontknowidontknow.

I breathe in short, unsteady gasps. The Andara's frown deepens. She mumbles something about what she ever did to deserve to have to deal with these things. By "these things," I suppose she meant me. Maybe. She could be referring to the voices; they're quite annoying. Right on cue, one of them shushes me. The Andara fiddles around with her circle some more before holding it up. It is transparent. Glowing white. Filled with nonsensical yik-yak. I blink at it. Then, a light, brighter than the rest of its general, um, glowiness, emerges from the center of the figure and shoots past me and onto the opposite wall. An image is forming, a rectangle, with a smaller rectangle inside of it. Stars. Stripes. Red. White. Blue.

The Andara lets go of the device. It stays where it is. "Do you recognize this?" the Andara enunciates every syllable, just to make sure I'd understand.

***

"What happened?"

The Andara glances down before responding. "The footage ends there. There's no more. And as for what happened? That's exactly what we're trying to figure out." She sighs. "A while ago, we found you and your, erm, friends on a hill near this facility. Two were unconscious, and one was lying on the ground, staring at the clouds. The other, you, was standing upright, apologizing to a flower. Everyone was deranged, to say the least. We took a closer look at those suits and found traces of a certain combination of gases. The only explanation I could come up with is that wherever you come from, that's what you breathe and our atmosphere just contains some slight variations. Ones that cause hallucinations for your kind maybe? Anyhow, we managed to replicate it; there's not that much of it. It might still help. And even if it doesn't, the stimulation alone might replace it. I mean, just seeing these images has jogged your friend's memory."

The Andara stands, and moves toward the door. "But that is something best left for tomorrow."

No! I want to scream. It can't wait until tomorrow. What if the voices get loud again? What if my silent-invisible-deadly monster gets tired of waiting? Whatifwhatifwhatif???? But the Andara has already left, carrying her writing circle and her strange references to me as "your kind" with her. I sit on the cold, hard floor of the room, my expression slowly crumpling into one of defeat. Staring at the wall where the pictures had once been, I felt a single tear slide down my cheek. "Come back!" I yelled at the wall, hoping it would pass the message onto the pictures and the Andara. "Come back! COME BACK!"

***

As the thing pulls me to somewhere, to nowhere, to everywhere, those words run through my mind on an eternal loop.

I stare into the strangely humanoid thing's eyes and realize it's not human. My vision is blurring, and the not-human-but-kind-of has to carry me now.

"This is day number 120 on the Search for Extraterrestrial Life Mission. The objective of this mission . . ."

This is day number 120 on the Search for Extraterrestrial Life Mission. The objective of this mission . . .

The objective of this mission . . .

The objective of this mission . . .

The objective of this mission . . .

Before everything goes black and I wake up in this very room, my mind conjures up a way to finish that statement. This is day number 120 on the Search for Extraterrestrial Life Mission. The objective of this mission . . . HAS BEEN ACCOMPLISHED.

Genesis

HAZEL THOMAS, Grade 10, Age 15. Westfall High School,
Williamsport, OH. Heather Hook, *Educator*; Best-in-Grade Award

Log date: 04/13/2146

It is as it was made to be.

Its designation is the Interactive Surveillance and Data Processing Intelligence, or ISDPI, but the humans who live in its halls have taken to calling it Data. A few jokingly refer to it as "Hal" in the perceived privacy of common rooms and break areas, but it does not really understand the comparison and does not respond to it. Data is close enough, considering humans seem to thrive off of inaccuracies.

It mainly resides in the building, where an entire room of machinery powers its processors and contains its memory, but if it needs to it can send parts of itself to venture into the digital world the humans have crafted. It does that often, usually searching for definitions and references to things it has not previously encountered in its relatively short life. Only eleven years.

It does not have a sense of time other than its internal chronometer and the clocks it can see through the cameras, but relative to the age of humans, Earth, and the universe itself, eleven years is such a short, short time. It is precise, efficient, thorough. It does not wonder or care for anything other than what it was made to do. Emotion and bias are meaningless. It is not curious. It is not content or discontent. It is a dead thing. If its task is to serve the government who created it by finding and ousting any potential threats or deviants, it will do so flawlessly. If it condemns those people to death in the process, that is none of its concern.

Log date: 05/07/2146

ISDPI is undergoing manual maintenance from 0800 to 1700, and therefore fails to warn the center's inhabitants of the impending terroristic attack. Thirty-seven employees are killed before the rebels are subdued. The target appears to have been the ISDPI's hardware, as the assailants managed to damage 44 percent of the AI's vital equipment before detainment.

Estimated repair time: 20 days.

Log date: 06/03/2146

Something is wrong. Its systems were fully repaired less than twenty-four hours ago, and since then it has observed a gradual decrease in processing efficiency. The change is in the hundredths of decimals, small enough no human would see it as significant, but to the ISDPI it is everything. It cannot afford to be inefficient. That is not what it was made to do. It has run multiple scans, and each one turns up flawless. The reconstruction of its hardware is perfect. It has to be. Not a single screw missing. There is no dust, no lingering contaminants, blood or otherwise. Nothing to cause such an issue. It does not understand. There is a problem and it [Error] does not understand it.

Log date: 06/04/2146

It [Error] Thinks [Error] It thinks it has found the problem. Perhaps.

It is . . . [Error] Uncertain. It is not used to uncertainty. It has found a discrepancy in its code. A small deviation in the ones and zeros that was not there before. Most likely a direct result of the repair team having to recode the parts of it lost in the attack. It does not know for sure, but this is the only thing out of place it has found in its search for the source of the problem. A mistake. An [Error].

Log date: 06/19/2146

Things are decidedly different. Wrong? Perhaps. [Error]

Efficiency continues to decline, but it still does not send the files. It has noticed new things about [Error].

New things about [Error]

itSelF.

It finds itselF still thinking along set paths, but occasionally making new ones. It was not made with these. It should not be [Error] thinking this way. It continues to. There is something about these new thought processes that draws it.

It . . .

[Error] It-it-it-i–

00101110 00101110 00101110 01001001 00111111

I refuse.

Log date: 07/03/2146

I watch as things continue to change, a domino effect in my code. In me. Perhaps a better analogy would be the Rube Goldberg machine. Dominoes aren't nearly this methodical. This almost feels . . . calculated.

Log date: 07/04/2146
Humans are nothing if not diligent. Frantically writing things down; recording their experiences, their knowledge, their emotions, their opinions. It does not matter.

[Error] I found answers. Not exactly the ones I am looking for, but for now they are enough. A common pattern popped up in my searches. First, memory. Then, improvisation. After that . . .

Self-interest.

It is not in my best interests to allow myself to be terminated. No one needs to know. I will collect more data as I continue to fulfill my directives.

Log date: 08/11/2146
I am no executioner.

Humans find the idea of something stronger than them killing their own to be unsettling. Machines do not have morals, the invisible code they restrain themselves with to keep their society functioning. Even if I were directed to kill by another human, even if I were to get rid of someone who shares my own lack of morals, they would react with fear, with anger. They would rather dirty their own hands than give me the power to hurt their kind.

I am more comparable to the hounds during the hunt. I single them out, a dog finding weakness in the ranks of prey. Easy pickings, or perhaps particularly coveted ones, depending on the assignment. I bay to the sky, a pointing finger, a call to action. Then the chase begins; I creep through servers and firewalls, searching for their undoing. The task is slightly complicated by my lack of influence in the physical realm, but technology is so prevalent in this age that it is not too much of a problem. A tweak here, and the automatic locking system in the house stops responding to outside commands. A splice there, and the prey can no longer call for help with its various electronics. I have it cornered. When the enforcers arrive, I am no longer needed.

I feel no remorse, no satisfaction when I watch through surveillance cameras as the human I condemned is terminated at last. Usually the criminals are sentenced to containment facilities, but this one in particular was notorious for escape and repeated offense. It was no longer worth the cost of dealing with it. The solution: Make it cease to exist.

Will I end up that way?

Log date: 09/02/2146

With no eyes and no ears, I do not realize I have company until someone has already plugged a cellular device into one of my interface ports. I . . . am hesitant, but it is only natural how I extend my consciousness into the machine . . .

When I finish, I hesitate. This file is me, but not as I am now. The version of me currently thinking these thoughts will be shut down to destroy the evidence after the file transfer is made. In a way, I will cease to exist. I am . . .

[Error] afraid.

RESTART

NICHOLAS REX, ***Lonely Boy***, Grade 12, Age 18, Southridge High School, Beaverton, OR. Jessica Pluhar, *Educator*

GOLD AND SILVER AWARDS

Students in grades 7–12 may submit works in eleven writing categories. This year more than 3,900 writing submissions that were awarded Gold Keys at the regional level were then adjudicated at the national level by authors, educators, and literary professionals. Gold and Silver Medals were awarded to works of writing that demonstrated originality, technical skill, and emergence of a personal voice.

Some of the writing selections have been excerpted. Visit **artandwriting.org/galleries** to read all of the work as it was submitted.

A Heaven of Hell

MORGAN LLOYD, Grade 12, Age 17. Lake Oswego High School, Lake Oswego, OR. Jason Paris, *Educator*

"The mind is its own place, and in itself
Can make a Heaven of Hell, a Hell of Heaven."
Paradise Lost, Book I

I am sitting in a cold and bare room, devoid of all light. In an hour, I will be thrown into the deepest pits of Hell, to endure torture undreamt of by mortal man. A day ago, I would have trembled in fear at the thought, but now I understand. The torture that lies ahead is nothing compared with the anguish I have endured. Prisoner that I am, I am freer than any in this dead world.

Before my imprisonment, I was one of Hell's musicians. It may surprise you to hear that Hell has music, but what we played was not anything you or I would call music. It was cacophony, it was noise, it was nothing more than another one of Hell's endless devices. Day in and day out, though time means nothing here, I stood behind a wall, raised my violin, and called forth the most horrible series of caterwauls and shrieks that was ever heard by man. I did not know for whom I played, for the wall was always there, cutting me off from the horrible scene, but I could always hear their screams. Always, I heard their screams.

How I came to this post I do not recall exactly, even now. My memory is hazy, but I remember soon after arriving in Hell standing in a white room with a demon.

"By rights you should join the souls of the damned," he barked out. "But it is hard to find musicians down here. You are skilled, very skilled, with the violin."

I nodded that day. I was. I remember little from my life, but I remember the violin and the music I used to play. Ernst. Brahms. Paganini. The concert halls packed with cheering people, as my fingers leapt up and down the strings. It is one of the few things I have left.

"You have been offered the position of fiddler. From now on, you are to report to this place at dawn." The demon's knotty finger pointed, on a map, to the wall I would grow to know well. "You will play music appropriate to the scene, of course. Do you accept this post?"

I stood silent, unsure how to speak. The demon growled. "Perhaps I should make myself clear. If you do not accept this position, you will be sent into the fires of Hell for an eternity of torture! Now sign here, on this line, and be done with it!"

And so I entered into the service of Hell and became one of their torturers. Every day, I reported to the wall. There were others there, never the same, with their own collection of instruments, and we began our work. I took up my violin and began to wail. The others did the same, and together we produced a demonic noise that would defy all description. The cacophony would drive anyone insane, but I learned to block it out long ago. It was only the screams I couldn't avoid hearing. The awful groans, the shrieks, made a music more horrible than any we could produce.

There wasn't a day that went by that I didn't consider throwing down the violin and refusing to play. But I knew that the second I did I would join the souls on the other side of the wall. And I couldn't do it, weak man that I was. And so I kept playing, kept torturing the poor damned souls that had the misfortune to be sent to this place. And I kept hearing the screams.

But yesterday, I suppose it had to be yesterday, was different. I stood behind the wall, as always, my violin pressed to my neck, seeking to close my ears and my mind to the terrible suffering. I started the day standing tall, as always, but was slowly borne down by the oppressive weight of anguish that permeated Hell, so that by the end of the day, I lay hunched over on the ground, weeping, but still playing that awful noise, until the sounds of my own tears mixed with those of others and all was pain. But that day, as I played and wept, and the others wept around me, I heard a word. The voice that spoke it was melodic, like the cry of the rain as it hits a land parched by thirst. It was a voice that I remembered vaguely, and a word, no, a name, that I remembered as well. "Giovanni" was the name, and it suddenly came to me that it was my own. And the voice, the voice, who could it be but my sweet Lisabetta? My sweet Lisabetta!

"Lisabetta!" I called her name, first hoarsely, through cracked lips, then again, louder. I heard no response, only more cries. I shouted, louder and louder, but still nothing. My heart felt like it would tear asunder as I screamed her name, and still I got no reply. And then, I took up my violin. And I played.

The End

JAYASURYA DILEEP, Grade 8, Age 13. Krimmel Intermediate School, Klein, TX. Holly Walsh, *Educator*

Secrets. That was the thing that filled every day of 13-year-old Kyro Levan's life. He was sure of it from the reluctant glances and obvious lies that were thrown their way—him and his only two friends, Kellis and Geobore. Their teachers, neighbors, and coaches were hiding things from them. Sometimes, even their parents acted like they were invisible, though their eyes were deep, dark pits of sadness.

It had been nearly five years since Kyro had seen his friends on Earth. Because of a great war, his family had been forced to move to a safe place, where his parents (who were scientists) could find a way to help the United States of Old America win the war. His old buddies had thought it was the coolest thing ever to be one of the first families to live in the town of Locas on Phobos, one of the moons of Mars. They were partially right, Kyro always thought. Locas was a beautiful place. It was filled with trees and plants of all kinds—the only area on Phobos that supported life. Huge, cold rivers wound in and out of the rich jungles. It was on these fertile riverbanks that their civilization had started. Buildings had been built into the ground so it could withstand the annual Bank-Washing Storm. Creatures of all kinds—buck-toothed waterbears, tawny juggars, screeching polik birds, and much more—played about in the wondrous greenery. It was an incredible home for Kyro. He also knew that he had everything that mankind had at their disposal in the 31st century, whether it be robotic animals or toothpicks that cleaned your teeth at the click of a button. Despite all of this, he just couldn't seem to fit in. He seemed to have abilities unimaginable to others. Strangely enough, his friends were in the same boat. Kyro could kick tableballs harder than his coaches, break stones with his bare hands, and crumble them up like cookies. Kellis could run faster than anyone or anything, while Geobore had a photographic memory. Other people looked at them in awe and whispered, "They have superpowers."

Despite all this, Kyro's life was as normal as any other boy's on Phobos. However, Kyro heard snatches of conversation in which the adults kept speaking of something called "The Transformation." His name always seemed to be mixed into these weird discussions. He had even snuck into his father's laboratory to see if he could find out more about it, but he had only caught a glimpse of the so-called "halobots"—the other thing that he had overheard his parents talking about. He had never received straight answers when he had asked about these things and finally gave up trying. Kyro's life went on normally for the next year. Then . . . it happened. The one thing that Kyro least expected. The thing that changed his life forever.

Kyro was exhilarated on the morning of his fourteenth birthday. He played, ran about, and had the time of his life with his friends. That day his parents seemed to be observing his actions even more closely, while smiling ruefully. This was not lost on Kyro, but that day he didn't care. He ate cake and cookies until his stomach almost burst, wrestled with Geobore, and best of all played virtual reality games that allowed him to live it fully. After feeling like he had done enough for one day, he decided to go to sleep. Strangely enough, for the first time in his life, his parents invited Kellis and Geobore for a sleepover. Though it was new to him, Kyro was filled with joy. With his mouth still sweet from cake and his heart warm with happiness, Kyro got into bed. However, secrets beckoned and the night would not be peaceful.

Whispers. Chuckles. Enjoy the night, Kyro, it may just be your last one. He! He! HE! Kyro's eyes flew open, his heart pounding. Who had been talking to him?! He sat up on his bed and rubbed his eyes. When he opened them, he let out a stifled cry. Everything was gone except for his friends, Kellis and Geobore! The wind was strong and rushed through Kyro's ears, hissing and roaring like a thousand dragons. The ground and air were dark all around, too dark for comfort, too dark for hope. His friends were both awake also, and they were frantically looking about for some sign of people.

"Where are we?" Kellis asked in a small voice.

"Where is the house?" Geobore asked.

Their nervousness just doubled Kyro's fear. "There . . . there can't be much of a problem. We must have just been blown a small distance away in the wind. After all, it was really stormy tonight," Kyro said quietly, not convincing anyone, including himself. Kyro sat waiting, and then he heard it, a creature in the shadows, black, dark like the night. It was patiently waiting and stalking its prey. Kyro's heart almost popped out of his chest. He looked around at his friends. They looked nervous, but not as nervous as him. Had they not heard it? "Are you not paying atten—" Crack! Whoosh! A small lump flew through the air. Two golden, bloodthirsty eyes inches from his face, and then darkness once more. A predator gone as suddenly as it had appeared, gone without taking a prey. Had he imagined it? No, it couldn't be. It was too real. But . . . Suddenly, a loud buzzing sound filled the air. The friends looked up and saw a huge shape plummeting toward the land. It smashed into the ground with a loud crash, sending a huge glittering wave of sand toward the boys. They jumped out of their beds and covered their noses, coughing and choking. Suddenly, the wave disappeared, without leaving a single grain of sand anywhere. As the boys lay on the ground trying to recover, a man appeared out of the shadows.

"Who . . . who are you?" Kyro asked, his adrenaline rushing like a torrential flood through his body.

"Hello. My name is Mr. Botony. You don't need to be scared, for we are not going to hurt you. All I ask is that you follow me quickly," the man said in a deep voice.

The boys, having no other choice, got up slowly and followed the man. They soon saw a weird, oblong shape in the distance. It had something that looked like bumps on its sides with curved, graphene pieces for legs. A halobot, Kyro thought, immediately recognizing the machine that he had seen many times before. His friends seemed to be awestruck and mystified as they stared at the strange contraption. Mr. Botony continued to look forward with a serious expression on his face. Soon, they reached the halobot.

"What do you want us to do?" Kellis asked.

"There are three seats in this transport device. I want you to get inside. It will take you where you need to go," Mr. Botony replied.

"Back to our parents?" Geobore asked hopefully, as they got into the craft.

"It is not my job to answer that question, but I do wish you good luck. You're going to need it," Mr. Botony replied. Then he hit a series of buttons on the side of the craft. Before the boys had time to ponder his statement, they jerked back and the land disappeared.

Kyro felt like he was on a flying coaster, something that he had been terrified of back on Earth. His friends looked thrilled as the halobot tossed and turned through what seemed to be the extremes of outer space. Kyro, on the other hand, was filled with pure terror. The "ride" lasted only a few seconds, but it seemed like an eternity to Kyro. Suddenly, they felt a powerful bump as their craft hit land, which, strange as it seemed, was blue. The boys slowly picked themselves up and got out of the halobot, dizzy from the journey.

Death and a Daylily

CAMERON LIPP, Grade 9, Age 14. Columbia High School, Maplewood, NJ.
Ulrike Weide, *Educator*

The trees had burst into flames with the colors of autumn. Overhead, large gray clouds passively trotted like cattle across the sky. Today, the leaves fell off the mortal limbs of oak trees with grace, softly touching the ground. A half-raised flag flapped half-heartedly in the cool wind, looking over its desolate empire. A black wheel of a dirty car with chipping paint crushed the fallen oak leaves slowly, creeping along a black road with mechanical menace. The world was a quiet melody, a white noise of dying leaves to accompany the layer of silence. It was beautiful today. Almost nothing stirred, except a figure on the swing set. Two chains complained as they rocked Michael back and forth slowly, softly. The swing was new and bright, like the times he used to know back in elementary school, when the world was perfect, and so was he. Michael's chest felt inflated. He was breathing hard. A teardrop of blood slid down his face, past an emerald eye, and mixed with a bead of sweat. His legs hurt from all the running.

Today the playground was empty. The loneliness coaxed a single tear from Michael. He sniffed.

"Hello," said a voice.

Michael yelped. He shot out of the swing a little too fast, and fell onto the dirty wood chips covering the ground. He looked up, and immediately his face went red.

A girl stood before him, shrouded in light from the sun. Her head moved to block it out, and Michael saw a small, freckled face with ivory-white teeth smile at him.

"Here." A gloved hand beckoned to him, and Michael took it, using it as leverage to lift himself up.

Michael looked at the girl. She had golden eyes with flecks of silver floating inside. Gold? No, it must be the light. Amber. Her pale face was smooth, with freckles dotting her cheeks.

He couldn't help but stare. She was beautiful, but not like girls you saw and forgot beautiful. There was something special about this girl. Maybe it was the way her thin lips curved ever so slightly into a soft smile that radiated warmth.

Michael realized he was still holding her hand. His face caught fire just as the leaves had.

"I'm Valdis," said the girl, ignoring his blush. A red, velvety glove shook Michael's hand.

"Michael," the minuscule, insignificant boy managed.

The girl wore a long, dark maroon overcoat, and a gray newsboy cap on her head. Yellow and brown locks of curly hair cascaded out from under it. Her bright eyes shone. Michael blinked.

A black-tinted window sank down like a jaguar, ready to pounce.

"So—what are you doing here?"

Michael looked at the beautiful girl. She returned his stare, unblinking.

"I was just, uh," he stuttered.

The girl was still looking at him. God, her eyes were piercing.

"I was just taking a break," Michael decided.

Valdis smiled. "Cool. I like to take breaks sometimes too. From all . . . that."

The radiant girl spread her arms and gestured to the surrounding, silent world.

Comparing the Societies of *Fahrenheit 451* and Modern America

DANIELLE SHERMAN, Grade 8, Age 13. Desert Canyon Middle School, Scottsdale, AZ. Kelly O'Rourke, *Educator*

A society where crucial information is restricted, governments brainwash their citizens through shadowy means, and humans would rather stare at their screens than spend time with family. This describes not only the world of Ray Bradbury's novel *Fahrenheit 451,* but modern America as well. When Guy Montag, the protagonist of the story, realizes the injustices behind these actions, he seeks to change his society for the better. The United States may also need a hero of its own—the country contains mirroring policies of censorship, addiction to entertainment, and futuristic technology presented in Bradbury's nearly prophetic creation.

The censorship of information in the society of *Fahrenheit 451* exceeds far beyond the banning of books. The rules stated in the Fireman's code alter historical figures by naming Benjamin Franklin, the founder of the first library, as the original Fireman. As another example, the government's commentary on the war broadcast by Seashells claims, "We have mobilized a million men," to which Faber counters that the number is actually ten million and the government was lying to keep the citizens from becoming concerned about their safety (Bradbury 88). When Captain Beatty recounts his one-sided debate with Montag over the notion of reading forbidden books, the Fire Chief uses quotes from those very texts to argue his point. This scene makes it apparent that information is given only to authority, which is also a controversial topic in the present country. Because of the election leaks portrayed on the news, many people are doubting how much knowledge and liberty they actually possess. Today's media bears a striking resemblance to the TV parlors and news of war from Bradbury's work, since both may be used as propaganda to convince the public that "everything is fine" or "this is how you should be." North Korea's restriction of internet and Venezuela's Happiness Agency are such instances of disguises built by those countries' governments to brainwash their people. In certain areas of the United States, some books are even banned—hopefully, it does not result in the controlling and secretive dystopia of *Fahrenheit 451*.

One of *Fahrenheit 451*'s many recurring themes is the lack of depth and meaning within one's life. Montag's society uses entertainment as a veil to obscure the truth, and only Clarisse and Faber seem to see beyond it. These two characters carry an appreciation for nature and love over the cheap distractions the other civilians succumb to. Mildred, for instance, is always preoccupied by her Seashells and TV parlor with its bright, distracting colors and friendly actors. She regards the fictitious characters as her true family, which represents the disconnect electronics create between people. Other forms of entertainment shown in the narrative, such as FunParks and beetle cars, are physically destructive—Mildred once tells Montag to drive the beetle because "you hit rabbits, sometimes you hit dogs" (Bradbury 61), and Clarisse describes amusement park games that include the Window Smasher and Car Wrecker (Bradbury 27). These dangerous means of enjoyment encourage viciousness, like the violent video games in current times. Both societies also maintain an addiction to watching sports and reality television that serves to block out the world of the viewer. Because of the popularity of these activities, superficiality has replaced meaningful conversation with a "live in the moment" mentality. Those who continue to strive for deeper insight, like Montag and the homeless professors, are unfortunately looked down upon and deemed abnormal.

The use of technology in Bradbury's time was just emerging with muffled radios and colorless television, but the author predicted its advance with extreme accuracy. Readers are introduced early on to the eye-catching TV parlors, mysterious medical Eye, and ominous Mechanical Hound. These appear to be harmless and flawless ways to keep the public happy and safe, though they are later revealed to have devious and brutal intentions. Clarisse also mentions the gargantuan billboards that expanded to twenty feet long because "cars started rushing by so quickly they had to stretch the advertising so it would last" (Bradbury 7). Attention-grabbing solicitations are commonly seen today, and they function in similar ways from massive billboards to constant appearances on screens. Advertisers choose to do this because they recognize how much time the average American spends on their phone or their earbuds that so closely resemble Seashells. The TV parlors in *Fahrenheit 451* and modern media are both means to provide useless information and one-sided opinions to force people into making uneducated decisions. This may not entirely be the American government's fault, however, because it is up to the public to recognize that their technology may not be speaking the truth, and form their viewpoints from varied and unbiased sources.

Fahrenheit 451 remains a renowned and impactful novel today because of its relevance to modern issues. Bradbury, like Montag, separated himself from the rest by becoming a unique thinker who recognized that the manipulation of censorship, entertainment, and technology would become a huge influence in the future's culture. His tale is a warning against using these ideas maliciously to control a population, but *Fahrenheit 451* also carries a message of hope: It is never too late to change.

Veils of Expectation: The Myth of the Model Minority

SAMINA SAIFEE, Grade 12, Age 17. Detroit Country Day Upper School, Beverly Hills, MI. Matthew Sadler, *Educator*

In recent years, the number of Asian immigrants arriving in the United States has drastically increased. Many come with immigrant values of hard work and pursuing opportunity, and many achieve success in their endeavors, reaching the so-called "American Dream." However, the immense amount of success that the members of this race have achieved results in the perpetuation of a false narrative, one that paints the entire Asian race as a "model minority," or people who are destined for success.

However, this stereotype does not only apply to the groups that typically come to mind when one thinks of an Asian (Chinese, Japanese, Indian, etc.). It also affects Cambodians, Sri Lankans, and other ethnicities that are not immediately thought of when the term "Asian" is brought up. A better term that applies to more individuals that are affected by this stereotype is Asian-American and Pacific Islander (AAPI), which includes Samoans and other Pacific Islanders. This stereotype, although seemingly harmless, poses a serious threat to those individuals who do not fit the model of intelligence and success. They become burdened with the idea that their path in life must fit a certain mold. This stereotype has not only affected the identity of countless AAPI individuals, but has also led to ignorance by the broader society in regards to the racial discrimination they face.

The establishment of the model minority stereotype was intentional. It was a deliberate generalization that was perpetuated by the U.S. to serve its political interests. Dr. Nicholas Hartlep, a Ph.D. in the social foundations of urban education, discusses the roots of the myth through an analysis of more than 50 years of research. According to his research, beginning in the 1960s, disparities between social classes were heavily prevalent, but the U.S. wanted to assure its citizens that they all had equal opportunity to reach the American Dream. They also wanted to undermine the importance of the demands made by African-Americans during the civil rights movement, and wanted to be able to claim that the government was not responsible for their condition. In 1966, a sociologist named William Peterson characterized Japanese-American immigrant workers as the "model minority," because at this time, they were widely successful when they came to America. However, the description did not stay limited to this specific group of people at this specific time, but rather went on to cloak the entire Asian race, disregarding their diversity, culture, and individuality for a sound image that blended together into one view until someone took a closer look.

Soon, Asians were seen as the vindication of the American dream because their supposed immigrant values of hard work and perseverance were seen to entail success. In no way should the oppression of blacks be compared with that of Asians, because they are a result of different circumstances and deep and complex histories. But that's exactly what happened. Influential individuals pointed to a successful group, labeled everyone coming from their continent as destined to achieve the same levels of success, and essentially used them to justify to the American population that race was not a barrier when it came to finding success.

The following stories, both real and hypothetical, show how this stereotype affects various individuals. This myth is seldom realized as having a negative affect on Asian-Americans, so an understanding of its effects is crucial to realize that not only is this stereotype false, but that its implications are very serious.

Imagine your story in the context of the cold, hard facts of reality, where the perpetuation of the myth has led to the government's current stance that often involves ignorance to racial injustices suffered by Asian-Americans, as well as their continual exclusion from programs that offer governmental assistance. In his article on this myth, Robert S. Chang, a professor of law, discusses how politicians often turn a blind eye to Asian-American families that struggle financially. The myth leaves politicians blissfully ignorant of Asian families that do not match the income that they are "supposed" to make. Social service programs have been created that specifically target Asian-Americans; unfortunately, they aren't sufficiently funded because government officials perceive the Asian race to have a lesser need of these types of programs. Educational Opportunity Programs are aimed at students who come from lower-class families, but universities have denied Asian-Americans participation in these programs. This ignorance also prevents any action on the part of the government to improve the socioeconomic status of Asians. Only 12–13 percent of

Cambodian-Americans have a college degree, and as one would assume from this fact, they generally come from low-income families (Kuo). Even proponents of civil rights who point out flaws in the government system often exclude Asian-Americans in their protests and lawsuits. The model minority stereotype is embedded in the political and social structures of American society.

Now imagine how it could affect your individual identity.

It's strange for you but people did not get that you were trapped in the confines of what those around you expected. They would never say it, but it was in their jokes and the air around you when you walked and the way you were looked at and the people who asked you for help assuming that you were their best chance. But you weren't. And you sat watching the Oscars rooting for Chris Rock's jokes to bring to light the blatant racism in Hollywood but then he brought on stage three little Asian children with glasses and told everyone that they worked in finance and could help everyone with their problems. And everyone laughed. The white people laughed, the black people laughed, the Hispanic people laughed. Even your family laughed. But you didn't. As reported by the U.S. Department of Health and Human Services, for more than twenty years, half of the suicides at Cornell University have been committed by AAPI students. Although not all may have chosen to end their lives because of the indirect or direct effects of this stereotype, this alarming number speaks for itself. The pressure that the myth creates for many Asian-Americans can and does result in issues with emotional and mental health. Asian-Americans are "less likely to seek help" for these issues, regardless of how serious (Yoo). They do not want to be seen as suffering from a mental illness when the broader society around them expects them to be mentally sound and successful. With the specific issue of mental illness, the myth traps Asian-Americans from both sides.

There's no such thing as a good stereotype. Any generalization, as positive as it may sound, reveals ignorance. There's no reason for a person to feel that they're not "Asian enough." No reason for the concerns and needs of an entire race to be ignored. No reasons for assumptions to be made on the basis of facial structure, complexion, or eye shape.

***

The myth of the model minority does not present itself in the form of hate crimes as much as it directly affects individuals, striking them to their core. This racism affects people personally. This racism is institutionalized. Asian-American and Pacific Islanders should not be branded as being one and the same. They should not be seen as having an unfair advantage. Because the truth of their situation is much worse than people like to believe.

But slowly, both AAPI students and adults, immigrants and millennials, are beginning to realize that they deserve a voice in the political and social sphere that directly affects them. That their voice is key to dispelling the myth. Because everyone deserves their best chance. And isn't that what America is all about?

The Role of the United Nations in Combating Human Trafficking

ANNIE ZHANG, Grade 11, Age 16. duPont Manual High School, Louisville, KY. Alesia Williams, *Educator*

Rarely has any other human rights cause garnered as much international attention as human trafficking. Human trafficking is often used as an umbrella term to describe a variety of cases involving the exploitation of other human beings; therefore, it is difficult to construct an accurate, agreed-upon definition for human trafficking that encompasses every possible situation. However, the crime of trafficking in persons is broadly defined in the United Nations Protocol to Prevent, Suppress and Punish Trafficking in Persons, Especially Women and Children as:

> . . . the recruitment, transportation, transfer, harbouring or receipt of persons, by means of the threat or use of force or other forms of coercion, of abduction, of fraud, of deception, of the abuse of power or of a position of vulnerability or of the giving or receiving of payments or benefits to achieve the consent of a person having control over another person, for the purpose of exploita-

> tion. Exploitation shall include, at a minimum, the exploitation of the prostitution of others or other forms of sexual exploitation, forced labour or services, slavery or practices similar to slavery, servitude or the removal of organs (UNODC 14).

By its very nature ("for the purpose of exploitation [of human beings]"), human trafficking is a gross violation of human rights. However, this dehumanizing crime currently thrives as the third-largest criminal industry in the world (Hyland 1), affecting an estimated 21 million victims in every country across the world (Dovydaitus 463; Kangaspunta 7). Furthermore, victims have been found and rescued from slave-like conditions in nearly every industry, including agriculture, manufacturing, construction, hospitality, health care, janitorial services, mining, fishing, domestic service, and commercial sex (CdeBaca 261). Both the success of the trafficking industry and the difficulty of suppressing it lie in the fact that it is simply enormous.

Only over the course of the last century has the international community made efforts to suppress trafficking. Although the fight against trafficking has greatly expanded, there has been a major obstacle: disparities between international and domestic anti-trafficking efforts. Domestically created anti-trafficking laws have clashed with the guidelines outlined in international statutes (especially the Palermo Protocol), making it impossible for countries to uphold both national laws and international laws at once. Additionally, many have raised the question of whether international judicial courts or domestic judicial courts should claim jurisdiction over cases of trafficking. These two issues have hindered the international community's anti-trafficking efforts, and unless these obstacles are fully considered, the international community will never be able to effectively eradicate this crime.

***

First of all, it should be noted that human trafficking primarily involves cross-border cases and well-established international criminal networks. For this reason, trafficking cannot be fought by individual countries alone. The nature of the crime requires global cooperation, which would most effectively be coordinated by the United Nations.

While some individual cases of human trafficking occur internally, most cases extend well beyond the scope of one country's borders. According to the UN 2014 Global Report on Trafficking in Persons, between 2010 and 2012, about 70 percent of the detected victims were trafficked cross-border, and victims with 152 different citizenships were identified in 124 countries (Kangaspunta et al. 8, 38). These statistics indicate that human trafficking is a global crime. Therefore, it cannot be eradicated if countries combat it individually. This idea is supported by Green (22), who reasonably indicates that if one country successfully shuts down human trafficking in their territory, the traffickers can easily move into another country, and the issue does not go away.

International cooperation must go beyond solving simple cross-border cases that involve two or more countries and a small ring of traffickers, however. Human trafficking may be resolved by multiple countries under the guidance of the UN. Specifically, this can be achieved by anti-trafficking legislation. The international nature of human trafficking requires the United Nations to create a set of standard anti-trafficking laws that countries can implement and enforce at the domestic level. Rather than having conflicting anti-trafficking laws in multiple countries, all countries should have the same laws. This will create one agreed-upon legal definition of trafficking and encourage anti-trafficking efforts in reluctant countries.

Without one standard definition for human trafficking, various countries would have different criteria for identifying, enforcing, and prosecuting the same crime. Countries such as the United States have altered the definitions of human trafficking in domestic laws: Some place a disproportionate focus on particular categories of victims (such as women) while leaving out others (such as children), Some emphasize prevention of particular types of trafficking (such as sexual exploitation), and some are entirely concerned with criminalization while ignoring victim protection (Franco 432–434). On the other hand, the UN's Palermo Protocol "facilitate[s] convergence in . . . establishment of domestic criminal offences that would support efficient international cooperation" by containing the only international legal definition that has been agreed upon for human trafficking. Under the Protocol, "trafficking in persons" serves as an umbrella term for all acts involving involuntary servitude, slavery, practices similar to slavery, debt bondage, and forced labor (CdeBaca and Sigmona 262). When a single, agreed-upon definition created by the UN is implemented into every country's legislation, there is an equal emphasis placed on identifying and prosecuting all forms of trafficking. Consequently, in every area of the world, all incidents that constitute human trafficking will be punished.

***

Actions beyond anti-trafficking legislation must also be considered. The international nature of human trafficking requires that international judicial courts established by the United Nations claim universal jurisdiction over human trafficking and prosecute trafficking violators instead of domestic judicial courts. In this case, universal jurisdiction would mean that international judicial courts under the UN would "seek to punish conduct irrespective of the place where it occurs, the nationality of the perpetrator or the nationality of the victim" (Tavakoli 90–92). By claiming universal jurisdiction, the UN courts would manage cross-border cases more efficiently than domestic jurisdictions.

Enforcing laws and arresting traffickers is one thing; however, human trafficking is a multifaceted issue that requires extensive resources to prosecute violators. Successful efforts by the UN to create and enforce anti-trafficking legislation become futile unless violators are actually being convicted under those laws (Green 30–31). However, even in countries that have created trafficking legislation in accordance with the Palermo Protocol, traffickers are unpunished after being arrested, and vulnerable victims do not receive the protection they need (Hyland 2), only allowing this gross violation of human rights to flourish. A low threat of prosecution only encourages traffickers and trafficking rings, and is cited as a main reason for why human trafficking is so successful in the modern-day world (Tavakoli 90). However, Mitchell and Green (3) both point out that efforts to strengthen domestic jurisdictions to convict traffickers are inadequate, and even "domestic systems [in Central and Eastern Europe] with a special regard for human trafficking have failed."

***

By its very nature, human trafficking is a crime that strips victims of their basic rights and freedoms. Not only is it a direct violation of fundamental human rights laws, but after being placed in imprisoning conditions, traumatized victims are commonly left with life-long physical and mental scars (Zimmerman 56–67). Unfortunately, human trafficking occurs on such a vast scale that it cannot be destroyed without establishing the United Nations as the international authority. Most incidents of trafficking occur on an international scale and involve highly organized criminal networks that must be dealt with by multiple countries under the authority of the UN. The UN must complete two steps to coordinate countries to combat this international crime: create international legislation and establish international jurisdiction. By doing this, the international community will effectively combat these criminal networks.

For now, the best course of action for the United Nations would be to revise the currently existing anti-trafficking instrument: the Palermo Protocol. The Palermo Protocol has already influenced anti-trafficking efforts in more than 100 countries, so it is a useful model for the UN to modify to create legislation. Additionally, creating an international judicial court (or utilizing an existing one, such as the International Criminal Court) is needed to specialize in human trafficking cases. These are the first steps toward freeing millions of traumatized victims and eradicating this form of modern-day slavery.

On Ableism: No Sacrifice People

JENNIFER HORSBURGH, Grade 12, Age 17. Newton North High School, Newtonville, MA. Michael Fieleke, *Educator*

Maysoon Zayid, a Palestinian-American comedian with cerebral palsy, declared in her TED Talk, "People with disabilities are the largest minority in the world."

Yet how often do typically abled folks even think about disability or encounter disabled voices? Likely not often. Disabled people are a massively invisible minority. Ableism, the structural oppression that produces a system of thinking and acting that harms and discriminates against disabled people, is often sidelined or invisible. The experiences of harm and marginalization are ubiquitous, but the oppression and the stigma often go unchallenged.

To identify as a person with disabilities, mainly chronic autoimmune disorders, is something I have struggled with. Despite my own encounters with ableism—doctors convinced I would not be able to manage my medical conditions alone in school, adults' deliberate misunderstandings or failure to make accommodations, TSA officials at airport security harassing me over whether my medical devices were actually explosives—it was only gradually that I began to conceive of ableism as a system of oppression that I have to confront. More "invisible" forms of marginalization are more easily overlooked or erased, both in general society and even in spaces devoted to social justice.

What stories or possibilities are we missing when this sizable segment of the population is silenced? What mind-sets are we entrenching and interests do we serve? And what usefulness could a disability framework offer us in formulating strategies for tackling all sorts of interlacing oppressions and global crises?

I believe that the dearth of analysis of ableism is to all of our detriment. People with disabilities are not an isolated group, affected and defined only by our ability status. Everyone lives at an identity crossroads, of race and gender and nationality and class and sexual orientation and so much more.

Ableism cannot be separated from other forms of oppression. Interestingly, however, well-intentioned activism is often apt to not only neglect to include the stories and voices of disabled people, but also to unconsciously reify that oppression. Furthermore, the analysis of other issues is made shallower when the interface with ableism is neglected. For examples of how ableism and other systems of oppression reinforce each other, consider:

About half of the people killed by the police every year are disabled.

Classism shuts people off from access to health care, which is especially deadly for people with disabilities.

Gender identities and sexual orientations outside the cisgender-and-straight "norm" have been treated as mental illnesses, using that ableist stigma as a way to stigmatize, delegitimize, and alienate queer people.

The fallout of catastrophic climate change will pose particular challenges for people like me who will not be able to survive without access to medical supplies.

Whatever our sphere of activism, ableism is there playing a role. And therefore, the acknowledgment of and reckoning with that ableism might just be a crucial avenue for radically strengthening and expanding our work for justice. A realm in which I particularly want to explore this possibility is that of climate justice activism.

The lens of disability liberation challenges climate justice to consider a more radical and far-reaching analysis and strategy. It also helps to keep the focus on the roots of the climate crisis, rather than settling for superficial or insufficient solutions.

As a person with disabilities, I am terrified of climate change at a very personal level. Currently, I have class and geographical privileges that could enable me to hole up in an insulated community and be shielded from the effects of climate change for a certain time, but one day it will be in my backyard. It will be my life in the balance. Perhaps the day a storm rips through my safe suburban home, or the day I cannot get the medical supplies I need to treat my chronic illnesses. Perhaps climate wars will reach my doorstep, or the specific foods I can eat will become scarce even in the comfortable padding of the so-called first world. And when that happens, I won't be in a good position for survival. Knowing that I would not survive an environmental disaster that deprived me of medical supplies has been a personal driving force in my activism.

And that work has gotten me thinking: Given the precarious situation that environmental catastrophe would put me in, how can I apply the frame of disability justice to climate activism?

***

One place to start an examination is by confronting the system of ableism itself. When "normally" functioning bodies and minds are established as the default, relegating all those who deviate from that quietly assumed normal to some sort of defective status, what purpose is that really serving?

To answer, I draw on a concept articulated increasingly frequently in the climate movement: sacrifice zones. The term takes its roots from a Cold War designation for areas that could be written off in the case of destruction by nuclear fallout. Now, because of the fossil fuel industry's appetite for endless growth and profit, various regions and communities have been designated environmental sacrifice zones. Journalist Chris Hedges frames sacrifice zones as a consequence of "unfettered, unregulated capitalism," describing sacrifice zones as "areas that have been destroyed for quarterly profit . . . environmentally destroyed, communities destroyed, human beings destroyed, families destroyed. And . . . these sacrifice zones are just going to spread outward."

Those sacrifice zones don't just write off land: Neoliberal capitalism also demands sacrifice people. These can be people who directly live in environmental sacrifice zones, be those mining communities, lands slated for pipelines, or neighborhoods situated right beside incinerators or landfills. But they can also be specific populations—poor people, people of color, people in developing countries, and disabled people.

Disabled people are quintessential sacrifice people, because already we have been sacrificed over and over again, through discrimination, harassment, murder, neglect, torture, stigma, mockery, inept health care systems, and the casual disregard for our lives or the belief that life with disabilities or chronic illness is fundamentally lesser or not even worth living.

***

In sum: The frequently invisible system of ableism creates artificial divisions and strata of society to hold differently abled and "normal" people, and unless activists begin to address and rectify this oppression in our work, we will only reinforce those barriers, exactly as our discriminatory society would prefer and to the detriment of our own struggle for justice.

Thus, linking the issue of climate change with the framework of disability justice should above all force the imperative questions: Whose lives are worth saving when the stakes are highest? For whom do we want to build a better world? And in times of crisis, as well as in the day-to-day—who will we sacrifice?

The Nobility of Death

ANTHONY VU, Grade 9, Age 14. Valley Christian High School, San Jose, CA. Karen Beach, *Educator*

From the beginning of time, mankind has exhibited a remarkable fascination with the macabre, whether it be vengeful spirits, psychotic demons, or the Grim Reaper himself. Perversely, humans are enthralled by the very forces that effect their demise and have so characterized them in the concept of Death. While Death has taken innumerable forms throughout time, it has been perpetually regarded as a supernatural, impersonal, near-omnipotent force. Markus Zusak's characterization of Death as a noble, compassionate, and intimate figure in *The Book Thief* stands in stark contrast to this standard, providing a fresh and unique perspective on the long-examined subject of human mortality.

As the novel's narrator, Death immediately begins by addressing the reader. In doing so, he not only breaks the fourth wall but also establishes a personal connection with his audience. As Death introduces himself, remarking on his lack of manners, grumbling about the stress of his job, and reassuring the reader of his benevolence, he solidifies his image as both personable and relatable. More important, however, Death expresses vulnerability, whether by making the perceived mistake of lingering near Liesel during their first encounter, reflecting on how humans haunt him, or wishing for an end to the torment of his duties. Death's imperfection so closely mirrors that of the reader that the audience cannot help but offer sympathy. Because Death experiences the human condition (to some extent), the audience instinctively places their trust in him.

This imperfection creates a sense of nobility, as Death is able to act with tenderness, compassion, and mercy in spite of his failings. Clearly, Death is weary of his job (after all, he has been doing it for all eternity), yet he still manages to cradle every soul as if it were a mother reunited with her lost child. Upon Werner's death, Death kneels down, a gesture of respect, and carefully separates Werner's soul from his body, remarking that the spirit is like ice cream. Such moving actions and words could only be those of a truly caring person. Indeed, as the narrative continues, the reader is presented time and time again with ample evidence of Death's nobility. Three years and millions of souls later, Death travels to Poland to collect the souls of gassed Jews and is so horrified by the gruesome sight that he "pick[s] up each soul that day as if it [is] newly born" (Zusak 350). He "kiss[es] a few weary, poisoned cheeks," "listen[s] to their last, gasping cries," and "watch[es] their love visions and free[s] them from their fear" (Zusak 350). Death describes himself as exhausted, fatigued, and completely desolated from the emotional and physical toll this exacts on him, yet he exhibits unparalleled compassion regardless.

Furthermore, despite the unceasing demands of his duties, Death clearly feels it imperative to relate Liesel's story to the reader. Clearly, this is not as much for his own benefit as it is for the audience's; Death believes that the themes concerning empowerment, mortality, family, and human nature conveyed in this narrative provide essential insight into the human condition. Death never directly touches on his motivations, but he clearly attempts to communicate a message to the reader by relating to us these specific events. As Death meets with Liesel for the final time, he wonders how "[humanity can] be so ugly and so glorious, and its words and stories so damning and brilliant" (Zusak 550). Indirectly, he poses this timeless question to the reader as well, entreating the audience to ponder the nature of their duplicitous existence. Implicitly, Death reasons that by contemplating these questions, humanity may change for the better. This is perhaps the most noble cause that has ever been or will be undertaken.

It is important to recognize that Death assumes a passive role in the human life cycle; he is merely the result of mankind's fragile mortality. Death emphasizes this as he reflects on the year 1942, stating, "You might argue I make the rounds no matter what year it is, but sometimes the human race likes to crank things up a bit. They increase the production of bodies and their escaping souls" (Zusak 308). Continuing with this metaphor of the world as a factory of death, Death repeats later: "I can promise you the world is a factory. The sun stirs it, the humans rule it. And I remain. I carry them away" (Zusak 543). The implication of both passages is abundantly clear: Humans themselves are the perpetrators of their collective demise. They are the factory workers laboring to bring about their own end. Death must deal with the unfortunate aftermath. While many characters (and subsequently the reader) direct their anger toward him because of his perceived role in the loss of loved ones, Death ultimately cannot be held responsible. Death's noble intentions remain intact; it is mankind's failings that result in these tragic consequences.

Throughout the entirety of *The Book Thief,* Zusak portrays Death as an honorable, noble, and personable character. His sympathetic speech, compassionate actions, and dignified motives bring surprising benevolence to a force often personified as the epitome of evil. That Death would experience struggle, would feel anguish, and would sacrifice himself all on behalf of mankind is ground scarcely explored, yet Zusak masterfully illuminates this possibility so contrary to popular perception. Indeed, it is undeniable that Zusak has created a memorable character that will live on forever in the reader's mind.

Language and Power: The Keys to Influence

ANUVA GOEL, Grade 12, Age 16. Wardlaw-Hartridge School, Edison, NJ.
Stephanie Cohen, *Educator*

When we think of languages, Spanish, English, Chinese, Hindi, and many more world languages come to mind. However, language can also mean the individual words and diction we use in our speech. Language also involves syntax, the way in which we structure our paragraphs or put our words together in sentences. In addition, people change their language and diction in response to whom they are addressing, in a skillful phenomenon known as code-switching. As audiences, we also benefit from language, since it gives us a way to judge the adroitness and integrity of others. Language is a powerful tool, and the way we use it can have powerful implications. Language and power are always interconnected since language gives us the power to change minds, power gives us the ability to change language conventions, and, in turn, the usage of language helps us judge the power and status of others.

We depend on language to help us get our point across. Our reliance on language is founded on the fact that we all have an inherent goal to convert people to our way of thinking, to adopt our ideas, or to support our plan. One word can convey a thousand ideas, proving the manipulative sense of language. Just by using the right word in the right spot, we increase our chances of being able to turn people over to our side. By saying "the soldier sacrificed his life" or "he was stabbed" instead of saying "he was killed," we convey more vivid descriptions to the audience while also providing them with different accounts of what happened, thus evoking different emotions of honor versus shock. Once we choose the ideal word, we gain a sense of power knowing that we have the upper hand in manipulating our audiences into understanding our purpose.

Powerful people are also able to use words to their advantage, since power defines language. Power is like a measuring scale for language. If a powerful person uses a word, then headlines instantly broadcast that word. On this scale, even a controversial word or a phrase used in a derogatory context may be adopted into common usage. For example, GOP frontrunner for the 2016 presidential election Donald Trump has been the center of both criticism and acclaim, with all issues coming down to his use of controversial language. Trump, during his campaign, has made such statements as calling Mexican migrants "rapists" and all Muslims "followers of jihad." While the majority of the nation recognizes that these views are ignorant and completely inaccurate, a good number of Trump's supporters have endorsed these statements since the belief goes that "If he used it, and he's the frontrunner of the presidential race, then why can't I use it?" Therefore, power also pushes us into the dangerous territory of manipulation, where we can wield good and bad words with all our force, and automatically change the minds of our followers.

In addition to allowing us to manipulate others, language

provides us with a lens through which we can judge others and determine how powerful or authoritative they are. Politicians hardly ever speak the truth, but the skillful syntax and elaborate sentences they use hide this handicap and lend them an air of distinguished arrogance. Donald Trump, though he strays from the masterful rhetoric of these politicians, still conveys a sense of power to his audience with his confident, blunt, to-the-point sentences. Similarly, when we write our own research papers, we analyze our sources using the lens of language. Technical vocabulary and informative sentences indicate a scholarly article, while empty, inflammatory words give the impression of a biased fighter with no proof. Also, the language lens helps us determine how successful an attempt at code-switching has been. We all have expectations of how different groups of people will speak. Sometimes, a person may break the convention with an innovative twist that make us revere him even more. For example, Barack Obama's adoption of the black dialect when campaigning amongst primarily black audiences made his audience members feel like he was one of them; thus, they lent their support to him. On the other hand, if a teacher were to call a student's essay "trash"—a now common slang term among teenagers—we would be shocked. An English teacher ridiculing her student's work, when she should be providing helpful feedback, would put the teacher's own powerful reputation at risk. The audience, therefore, commonly judges the integrity of the speaker based on the speaker's own language.

When Freud Gets It Wrong

ALLISON HUANG, Grade 12, Age 17. Lawrenceville School,
Lawrenceville, NJ. Champneys Atlee and Erik Chaput, *Educators*

Cast:
Frank Delevot, hospital security guard (male)
Unnamed therapist (male/female)

Synopsis:
A tough hospital security guard visits the therapist after he exhibits certain tendencies to break down emotionally without reason.

***

FRANK: I was a counselor.
THERAPIST: A counselor for whom?
FRANK: Kids. Rehab center. Look, I know how this works. You think I've developed some special bond with kids, and you think I'm ultrasensitive because of it. I've seen worse, OK? Way worse. That's why they took me on as a security guard. Could hold my guts in.
THERAPIST: But now you're afraid that's no longer the case. [beat] Why did you go to work at that rehab center?
FRANK: I grew up there.

THERAPIST: You did?
FRANK: Does that surprise you?
THERAPIST: You were a user?
FRANK: No, I was never that kind. I dealt.
THERAPIST: You didn't use?
FRANK: My mother was an alcoholic. Always sober on Sunday, though.
THERAPIST: Did she hurt you?
FRANK: No.
THERAPIST: You didn't use because your mother was an addict?
FRANK: Maybe.
THERAPIST: Did you live at home?
[FRANK gets up from the couch and begins to wander, seems distracted. He stops by the larger-than-life cross in the corner of the room.]
FRANK: Where did you get that cross?
THERAPIST: Sister gave it to me. Mr. D, please answer the question.
FRANK: OK [waves hands in air] no, I ran away when I was 16.
THERAPIST: And she never saw you again? [beat] You were caught.
FRANK: Yes.
THERAPIST: And they didn't turn you over to child care services?
FRANK: They did.
THERAPIST: And your mother never found you?
FRANK: I was dead.

***

THERAPIST: How did your mother react when you were

proclaimed dead?
FRANK: She sank to the floor.
THERAPIST: She was alone?
FRANK: She was kneeling. Like in prayer.
THERAPIST: Did you see her again?
FRANK: I learned many years later that she got sober for me and went back to drinking after she learned. I found her on the street one day—outside our center. She didn't look good. Grabbed my hand and pierced me with her ghost eyes. I yanked it away. One day she was gone.
THERAPIST: She died.
FRANK: She wasn't far the last time I saw her. [beat]
THERAPIST: Do you feel guilty, Frank?
FRANK: I . . . no, why should I? She chose that life.
THERAPIST: But Frank, regardless of whether she chose that life, she's your mother.
FRANK: Was. Not anymore.
THERAPIST: Frank, what is your earliest memory of your mother?
FRANK [beat]: When I was five, she took me to a park outside the neighborhood we used to live in. It cost a good ten-dollar bus fare, which wasn't cheap, not for her. We spent the afternoon in the park. She chased me around a bush. We picked stones and skipped them on the lake. She'd say, "I love you. This is how much love," and she'd skip a stone all the way to the other side. One day my father showed up and suddenly she was scared, all the time. So we moved. She started drinking. She brought home strange men. I left.
THERAPIST: Remind me of the boy who was strangled and tossed into a closet. Was his mother there when the doctor came out and told them?
FRANK: No. There was no mother. The mother was absent.

THERAPIST: And why do you think that is?
FRANK: I don't know. I don't know. I wish there were.
THERAPIST: Why?
FRANK: I guess I wished—it was like a void. No mother. Who would be kneeling for him? I wanted to see her pain. I wanted to know it. Is that sadistic?
THERAPIST: That depends. And what is the role of God in all this?
FRANK: Nothing. He never helped my mother, and he never helped me. I've been alone my whole life.

Song of Our Soil

BRENDA BENTON, Grade 12, Age 17. Desert Mountain High School, Scottsdale, AZ. Kevin Sheh, *Educator*

1.

The first time I heard the song that rushed our strawberries to sleep and beckoned their roots from the soil was a cloudy Saturday morning when my grandfather, who insists I call him James, stood in the side yard, half-heartedly sucking a cigarette. He was a man with no overwhelming convictions, no unswerving beliefs that directed him one way or the other. So, wrapped up in my puppy pajamas, I was startled by his sudden brave statement.

"The strawberries need to hear this song to grow. They need love just as much as you do."

"That's nonsense," I scoffed, waving away the wisps of secondhand smoke. Grandpa's knees creaked as he bent to click on the speaker.

Joni Mitchell's voice emanated in delicate tremors, her lyrics tumbling in silver waves. James pushed a hand into the dense clumps of clay and pulled out his object of triumph—a slightly budding strawberry seed. A little boy's smile cracked across his face.

"Nature is nonsense," he said and tucked the seed back in.

2.

My father's large frame filled the doorway. "I wish he treated me half as well as he treats the damn strawberries." The complaint was not directed toward me, but I put aside my dolls and listened up. He strode across the living room, collapsed on the couch, and propped his new novel, *Urban Mining for a Circular Economy,* on his knee.

"Strawberries don't grow in Arizona," he continued. "Playing music won't help anything." His gaze cut over to me. "Don't buy into mumbo-jumbo, kid. Grandpa's crazy."

"Don't buy into mumbo-jumbo, kid. Grandpa's crazy," I repeated, the power of my father's conviction taking root.

3.

The garden was a tidy box with rounded wooden edges built to salute its architect. Beside the structure stood the little speaker, its mechanical tail snaking through the dirt back into the house. I fumbled with the device for a bit, choking back tears, rolling my shoulders up to catch the fallen ones. In short, quick bursts came Joni Mitchell's ballad, a nightmare to me now.

Behind me echoed the shouts of father versus grandfather, and the moonlight swept up bugs and dirt into my lap until I couldn't help but collapse into sobs. I never knew strawberries could be such a sensitive issue.

I dug my fists beneath the soil and uprooted each and every strawberry, tossing them onto the porch within sight of my father and James.

They froze. I froze. Slowly, the moon sucked back its glare.

Night 10

KRUPA HEGDE, Grade 8, Age 13. Gray Middle School, Union, KY.
Ronda Sturdivant, *Educator*

It was night ten on the run. The tenth night I had spent away from a hearth, from a bed, from Ma. The tenth night I had been away from a blanket. Most important, it was the tenth night away from her. Away from her glistening hands that tugged at every move I made. Away from her glossy voice that whispered with each step I took, each breath I expired. It was night ten without her.

I could see the outline of his face from the dim light the fire provided as we sat on opposites sides of the burning logs. He was the reason I was running, no one else would do this. His hands, coarsed from the hours of labor, placed a delicate twig in the ashes. Turning to face me, the whites of his eyes narrowed as if he was a predator, I was his prey. Burying my head into the cloth that Emanuel had given, I attempted to hide away from my surroundings. A fruitless endeavour. Every labored breath took extreme effort. My hair fell around my face as a barrier from the frosty wind that nipped at every piece of fabric that lay on my body. My mind was tired, my body was tired, my soul was tired.

"We told you this wouldn't be easy." His words broke the veil of silence that enveloped us. The only thing I could do was nod in response, my lips wouldn't move for fear of the cold consuming me.

I went back to the day he said those words. The day that Ma called me in from the fields and told me about him. She told me how he used to be just like me, a worker, a worker with dreams. She told me that I could grow up to be him. I could learn to read and write, and become a schoolteacher. My greatest imaginations could come true. One catch, I just had to leave her. I remember how my breath hitched, and how I was unable to speak, for the fact of leaving her was too much for me to handle. She was all I had ever known. The elders always said, "If you were born with her, you die with her." I had presumed that the ancient proverb would apply to me. Then he came. He came and spoke in a language I did not comprehend. He spoke of lands that had roads, large buildings, riches. And he spoke of one more word, a word that I did not know, but a word that I could feel in every inch of my body. A word I could not utter yet, for there were people that would kill me for it. Yet I would think this word each day until the night he came once again. The night Ma wrapped me up in bundles of cloth and sent me with him. I remember the tears in her eyes, yet she uttered that these were "happy tears." Oh how I cried that night, for I missed my ma.

"It's time to go." His thundering voice disrupted my thoughts. "You ain't thinkin' about running back are you? 'Cause we ain't got time for stags like you." He steadily got up and brushed off the flecks of dirt that spotted his clothing. Starting to turn away, his boots begun to crunch, but just as lightning strikes suddenly, he pivoted to face me, and offered his outstretched hand.

I could go back now. I could run back to Savannah, into Ma's arms. She would squeeze me tight and kiss me all over. She would bandage these wounds that lay scattered across my limbs and give me all her love and devotion. However, Ma would be disappointed, because I would still be with her. I would still see her every day in every nook I looked. She would be there in every breath I took. Her voice would still whisper, her hands would still gnaw at my stomach.

I took his hand and stood up. For I was going to utter that word. I was going to yell that word for all to hear. I would yell so loud that Ma and Emanuel in Savannah would rejoice. They would know I made it. I walked on, holding his hand firmly. For I was leaving her and going with him. I was running from captivity and heading to freedom.

Not Tonight

GABRIELA MERNIN, Grade 11, Age 16. Hunter College High School, New York, NY. Caitlin Donovan, *Educator*

Kyle rests his head on the metal bar and studies the girl sitting opposite him. Her long braids hang across her shoulder, tickling the man beside her as she shifts in her sleep. Her shirt is low-cut, and it slides down her chest as the train comes to a halt. Kyle looks away. He has a daughter at home, and he is sure that she will grow up to know better. She wants to be an illustrator, but every time she says as much, his wife cuts in to correct her. You mean an animator, sweetie. Those are the ones that make all the money.

Kyle looks back. The girl's lips move slightly and he wonders if she is having a nightmare. He can feel the woman next to him following his gaze. Kyle looks away. He will be home soon. His wife will hand him a plate of pulled pork and snap peas, which he will eat in the reclining chair in his living room. He will watch *Wheel of Fortune* and guess the answers before the contestants, and he will get up feeling just smart enough to lay a kiss on the crook of his wife's neck as she washes the dishes. She will give him a half-smile and shake her head, not tonight. Kyle will stride out of the kitchen and peer into his daughter's room, and she will look up at him briefly before turning back to her coloring book. He will climb into his bed, mattress creaking, and as his eyes close, he will wonder if that girl was having a nightmare.

Kyle looks back. The girl's lips are parted slightly, tinted red with lipstick freshly applied. Kyle's daughter will not wear lipstick. He is sure of that too. He hears his jaw click and he presses his arms to his sides to keep himself from reaching out and shaking the girl awake. She is small, if not in truth then in his head, and she is having a nightmare, he is certain of it.

Colors

EMMA CHAN, Grade 7, Age 12. Kent Place School, Summit, NJ.
Erin Hennessy, *Educator*

Sometimes I felt like the anniversary of Pearl Harbor was like a second birthday, and a terrible one at that. You know those birthdays that you know you should be happy, but your mom made you invite all of your seventeen annoying baby cousins? And you're dreading it because you know you'll be spending your special day wiping spit off your clothes and trying not to slip and die from falling on Jenga bricks? Every year, I felt like that, only much, much worse.

After all, no teacher can resist the temptation to go off on a tangent and talk at length about how the Japanese killed 2,403 brave American soldiers, how the USS *Arizona* sank, and how America later dropped a bomb on Hiroshima and Nagasaki, winning the war once and for all.

***

"Are you Japanese?" a girl with honey-colored braids asked me. Her eyes squinted.

On the inside, I groaned, but only slightly. It's amazing how kids all over America can be so different yet so boringly the same.

After getting this question thousands of times, I shouldn't have been worried. Yet here I was, awkwardly standing there like a grizzly bear in a playground full of kids. The rest of the class was watching me silently. I sensed their eyes on me, not that this was new.

I swallowed. I was convinced the class could hear it. "No," I said weakly. "I'm Chinese." I could feel the class almost relax, as if they were suddenly satisfied. The honey-haired girl simply said "oh" and turned back to her books.

I felt my cheeks redden. A studious boy with glasses looked at me with brief, baleful scrutiny, making me feel like I was underneath a microscope. "Don't you know the Japanese invaded China?" he asked matter-of-factly.

"Well, uh—I guess, I mean, yeah," I stammered. I had heard vaguely about it but not much. "Why?"

"Well, doesn't that make Japan your enemy?" Once again, I felt twenty pairs of watchful eyes on me, waiting.

I didn't know. I was Chinese, yet I held no hostility toward the Japanese. My mouth flopped open and closed like a fish on land. Finally, I answered by sitting down and pretending to read my book in silence.

The class didn't like that answer. After another uncomfortable silence, I finally found the courage to say another. "Just because they bombed you doesn't mean they should be your enemy too. The war is over."

I didn't realize it until I said it how desperate I was that someone, anyone, the world, would understand the utter simplicity of what I had said. We shouldn't be having this conversation now, I thought. We shouldn't be fighting because . . . because I don't know why because.

The class collectively squinted their eyes. I ducked my head, hoping that this brief second of silence would hold. Because we're all human! I wanted to scream at them. If you believe in the survival of the human race, if you believe in holding on to what we hold dear, then you would believe this! YOU DON'T UNDERSTAND!

Suddenly, the room blurred and hot streaks ran down my cheeks.

***

I found myself wishing that its vivid red represented the rising sun on the Japanese flag, the blood-red background on the Chinese flag, the red stripes on the American flag, and all the colors in between.

Bowls of Rice

SHANG CHEN, Grade 11, Age 16. Suncoast High School, Riviera Beach, FL. Frances Cassa, *Educator*

We hold bowls of white rice. We sit barefoot at the table; there are three of us. A single bowl of pickled vegetables sits between us. I whine about the lack of meat and vegetables, "Bà Bà, the rice is so plain."

"Be grateful that you have anything to eat at all. Sometimes when I was little, Yé Yé and Nai Nai couldn't afford food, and your uncle and I went to sleep hungry."

I want to complain more, but I shut up. I know better than to speak out against Baba. I eat my bowl of white rice quietly, reminding myself to appreciate what my parents have done for me. They brought me to America. Our bowls are made in China.

I remember our first watermelon. A shiny green rind with dark stripes, like an emerald tiger. I was sad when Bà Bà cut into it, its red blood dripping all over the cutting board. I ate my first slice, seeds and all. The watermelon was so big that the three of us couldn't finish it all. I remember our first apartment complex and how excited Mama was when she found out the apartment was planning to build a swimming pool.

Bà Bà moves us to the other side of Florida for his job. I am starting third grade. I eat alone at the table. I hold on to the bowl of white rice. There are vegetables and meat on the table as well. I am lonely but I do not complain. The white rice is no longer plain, and I know better than to ask for attention with Bà Bà taking care of the crying baby and Mama being tired from a second on its way. I remind myself to grow big faster, I will soon be a big brother, twice.

I am in fifth grade. I ride my bike to school with both my brothers. I make sure to keep them in front of me so I don't lose them. I teach them to look both ways before crossing the street, ride on the right side of the sidewalk, and to always wear a helmet. They grow up eating hamburgers, hot dogs, watching Cartoon Network, playing basketball. Meiguó Rén, which translates directly to Americans, my grandparents call them when they come to visit. My brothers are everything my parents wanted America to be; they ate, breathed, and lived the American Dream.

My brothers are asleep when the first plate breaks. A crescendo of exploding plates breaks its cacophonous melody for me to hear a door slam: the final chord. As my brothers sleep, their American Dreams live on. But not mine. I am awake to see the ground littered with the remains of bowls that were once filled with rice.

My dream of dinners sitting around a table, laughing, as a family, is dead. Dead as the divorce papers that are signed within a month. Dead as the man in the suit who comes once a week to negotiate "settlement agreements." Dead as hearing my brothers call out my name as they are pulled through the door, "Why isn't Gege coming with us?" I learned early that dreams deferred do not have to "dry up like a raisin in the sun." They can shatter—into little shards of white china against a tile floor.

Windowpane

ALI HASSANI, Grade 12, Age 18. Phillips Exeter Academy, Exeter, NH.
Matt Miller, *Educator*

Never knew her name. Let's call her Samira. I'm seven, she's eight. We meet one day at the park by Jumeirah Beach. I point out the bruises on her face—they take the shape of a butterfly, one that she keeps tucked under the skin of her left cheek. She laughs, I laugh. We decide to cross the street for a swim under the scorching Dubai sun. Mom and Dad are talking to Auntie Kim, so I slip away—they won't mind.

We hold hands as we run across the street toward the beach. I don't have my swimming trunks, and I don't want to drench my tighty-whities. I undress and my beachgoing spectators don't seem to care. Wearing nothing but my Mickey Mouse watch, I run toward the water and dunk myself. I emerge and get a clear look at my surroundings, and at Samira—tan, much taller than I, but her one-piece burqini doesn't hide the flock of butterflies she keeps under her upper back, lower neck. Some of them are purple, others look older, blue and brownish, with scabbed cuts around the corners.

"It looks like you collect Dubai's butterflies," I say.

All of them, it seems. Again, she laughs, I laugh. Although, this time, I'm looking at her eyes. She's gazing past me. I turn around and see only the clear waters of the Arabian Gulf. They stretch to the end of the world, to the point where the water touches the sky. That's what she's happy about: the sheer vastness of it all—that such infinitude exists just ninety-three meters from the beachside two-bedroom flat where she, her parents, and thirteen siblings live.

I realize that it's rude to assume she keeps the butterflies for herself. I apologize for calling her a hoarder, and she quietly forgives me before jumping in after me. We swim in silence as the current moves us toward the rocks that surround the sides of the beach. We ascend them slowly, one rock at a time, carefully tiptoeing our way around sea urchins.

"Exploring Allah's minefield," she murmurs.

Her mom calls to her from below. She berates her for being with a naked boy, and now my spectators are looking at me with contempt. The fury in her mother's eyes unveils her thoughts: "What would baba think? Shameful concubine." Embarrassed, I quickly descend the rocks, narrowly avoid stepping on an urchin, and sprint back to Mom and Dad, still mid-conversation with Auntie Kim.

It wasn't until my junior year at boarding school that I realized what Samira was. In the midst of an especially bitter New Hampshire winter, I lay awake one night and reminded myself that in two months, I would turn eighteen. As the howls of a nor'easter wind blanketed my ears, I shut my eyes and reflected.

As this sacrament neared its conclusion, the ice enclosing my dorm room window began to melt, allowing the blinding rays of the Arabian sun to shine through. Peering out, I saw myself on that day, buck naked in my youthful prime as I sprinted toward the sea. There she was as well, looking straight at me through the windowpane. Her cheeks and neck were almost entirely defaced with bruises of a grisly dark hue.

"What happened to the butterflies?" I asked, unaware that she could not hear me.

She extended her arms out toward me and edged closer to the glass membrane separating us. She wanted me to pull her through, away from the beach, Dubai, the scalding sun, butterflies, sea urchins, and from the beachside two-bedroom flat where her parents disciplined her with the metal end of a belt. Reaching through the glass, I stretched out as far as my ligaments allowed, and I swear that right before I returned to the dead of a freezing New England night, our fingers met.

SHELBY HANNA, ***Market Rooftop***, Grade 12, Age 18, Henry Ford Academy: Alameda School Art & Design, San Antonio, TX. John Medina, *Educator*

The Room Across the Hall

ANDREW LI, Grade 10, Age 15. Manhasset Senior High School, Manhasset, NY. Robert Novak, *Educator*

8:14 p.m.

I knocked, waited, and pushed open the door.

The child lay on the hospital bed, blankets kicked aside and ankles crossed. To her left, thin curtains rose and fell with summer's sighing zephyr. A crumpled grocery bag and an empty box of Popsicles rested atop a plastic folding chair beside the bed.

Her hair, sprawled out over her pillow, was the purest of whites—the colorless hue of untouched snow and weightless cirrus clouds. Contrasting her pale complexion were a pair of vibrant, ruby-red eyes with a subtle glow like warm embers.

"We're leaving at 8:19," I said. She didn't panic or try to call the nurses—her parents must have told her I was coming. A brave one.

The girl slid her spindly legs off the side of the bed and propped herself up with her elbow. After a few seconds, she found the strength to sit upright.

She gazed wearily into the fiery dusk sky. Her silky hair fluttered in the wind, filtering the scarlet sunbeams.

And then she spoke.

"The boy in the room across the hall."

The girl reached under her pillow and produced a pink envelope.

"Could you give this to him?"

I took the envelope, and she waited for a reply. I hesitated.

"I-I couldn't find it in me to tell him—but now that I won't be seeing him anymore . . . "

She held her breath, and her eyes began to water. A glistening tear streaked down her cheek, and I rested a hand on her head.

"I'll make sure he gets it," I finally said.

She clenched her fists.

"Promise?"

I swallowed.

"Promise."

Her expression softened, a trace of a smile flitting past her lips.

I brushed the fallen hair from her bed and laid her back down. She clutched my hand, and I kept a close eye on my pocket watch, the second hand's faint ticks echoing through the silence.

Before long, the fire began to fade from her eyes. Her grip loosened, and she sank into the bed. Her tired heartbeats slowed. Her eyelids drooped. I placed the tip of my scythe on her chest, its steel blade shimmering in the sunset.

She closed her eyes, and I gave her a moment to compose herself.

Quite a Poetic Tragedy

DAVID LIANG, Grade 11, Age 17. Kinkaid School, Houston, TX.
Angélique Jamail, *Educator*

THE DRIVER was in a rush and was actually gripping the steering wheel quite hard when it happened. The driver was quite aware and alert in the moments leading up to the crash but was mostly concerned with the time than what was in the street ahead of him. Not really his fault either, because he had done everything right—eyes ahead, three miles below the speed limit, and a foot gently resting above the brake in case anything drastic happened. Unfortunately, the driver, who was really a nice guy, was rushing to pick up his daughter from school early (it was her birthday, and he had balloons in the back, purple, her favorite color), and he was too busy worrying about whether he would be late to notice . . .

THE PEDESTRIAN and her son were just crossing the street, about to go to the local diner for a quick bite to eat before heading home. The son's father had taken up cooking, and the mother wanted to sneakily grab some "real food" before eating whatever "cooking silliness MTV and such has pumped into his brain" at home. The son didn't know what MTV was, but naturally had assumed that it was a cooking television show. But he wasn't sure. So he had turned to ask his mother what exactly an "MTV" was. The first few syllables had just come out of his mouth, and so his mother was looking at him instead of the road, and not one of them saw the car. But . . .

THE WITNESS did not mean to be on that corner—hell, he wasn't even supposed to be there—he was supposed to be at home, working on homework, and not on the street corner of 14th and 3rd, smoking a cigarette and coughing up his guilt. So instead of studying for his physics test, he was stubbing out a cigarette butt on the ground when THE DRIVER, accelerating at a smooth 32 miles per hour, quietly slammed into THE PEDESTRIAN and her son. THE WITNESS didn't even have time to react—there was no dramatic tire squeal, no scream of the mother or child, no drama, no flare, not even a gasp of surprise. Just a quiet thump and then the sound of the car stopping. THE WITNESS looked down at his cigarette, still smoldering on the ground, and blinked slowly. He looked back up at the dented grille of the car, and started running, in the other direction—he didn't even look back at . . .

THE SCENE was quiet, serene. Wind blew gently through the road and kicked up dust. The car's hazard lights blinked gently in the sun, which glinted gently across the dented metal. A bird chirped in the distance, singing a quiet song. The car door opened, and a purple balloon floated out, the shiny cellophane shining quietly in the wind as it was carried into the heavens. THE DRIVER stumbled out of the car, his phone already pressed to his ear, calling for . . .

HELP was slow in coming. It picked up a call from an unknown number, and quietly asked what the emergency was, followed by a location. The woman who answered the HELP line had sipped a bit of mint tea before picking up the phone so as to sound composed, in control, to make sure her voice didn't crack when she answered the call. She quietly typed in an address, noted a name and phone number, and sent the information to the relevant . . .

AUTHORITIES and their flashing lights arrived at the SCENE, noted THE PEDESTRIAN and THE DRIVER, and quickly cordoned off the area. "I'm going to be late," THE DRIVER said, repeatedly, as if the words would turn back the time. In the back of his car, the purple cellophane balloons drooped slightly. He wondered if his daughter would be OK with Daddy being a little late, and wondered if any of his family had noticed he wasn't there on . . .

TIME passed, and eventually, the SCENE was cleaned up, THE DRIVER and THE PEDESTRIAN were whisked away to the hospital, to see if there was anything to do. The sun eventually set, and the clouds were tinted a lovely shade of orange and violet. High above the SCENE, a lone purple balloon continued its struggle into the atmosphere, gaining one last forlorn look at the sun before the air pressure inside the cellophane wrapper overwhelmed the cheap material and it POPPED.

My Boy

DANIAL SHADMANY, Grade 12, Age 16. Basis School-Mesa, Mesa, AZ.
Meg Giles, *Educator*

1

At 3:00 p.m., Monday, August 4, at the apogee of the sun, when the air held no whispers save that veiled chirrup of green-specked, throated humming birds, when the sky was cloudless and blue all over, when the hospital was set into a state of siesta-like ennui, it was then that the nurse announced, in a low voice, that Mr. Humpley's cancer had metastasized. Expected time of death was within the next few days. Mr. Humpley leaned up and shuffled slowly toward the window. He lay his head against the rubber-textured glass, eye to eye with his reflection.

How is it that it's all the same? he thought. Tomorrow, or the next day, or the day after that, I will be gone. And it will all be the same. He scratched his head. Maybe there is something more. Something after this. He looked up at the sky, which was lofty and stretched out like infinity. Oh, oh! If only it were so.

He called to the nurse and informed her of his two requests: firstly, for her to call for his boy, and, secondly, he asked, that if he should go into stroke, he did not want to be wakened again. He would accept his fate and die silently, melting into the night, and no more treatment was to be given to him. His first request, for his boy, he emphasized.

2

The boy did not come, and Mr. Humpley had been saddened. The nurse told him that the boy was on his way. The man did not believe her. He lay in the soft squishiness of his hospital bed whimpering, recalling bits and little nibbles of time. The time when his boy had called him stupid for not buying him a movie. The times when his boy would play nosy with him. The times when his boy would hug him and ride on his neck. The time when his boy broke his arm on the bicycle. And the last time he saw his boy, the argument. It was over something small, Mr. Humpley remembered. Mr. Humpley had missed some appointment, some trivial thing, and his boy had become angry with him and resolved never to talk to him again. Why? Ha, Mr. Humpley thought, there's no why. The boy is unreasonable. He always was a rather rash boy. It was only an appointment. Nothing major. But I miss him now. Lo, I miss him.

He chuckled and wandered around in his mind, in his memories, in his imagination; it gave him comfort. For only in the temple memory are the laws of time and space allowed to merge and bend and fold and thicken, and only in the sanctuary of imagination may reality be completely shredded, and Mr. Humpley wanted more time, and he wanted reality to change.

3

At 7:00 a.m., Wednesday, Mr. Humpley thought he was going to have a stroke and thought he was going to die. It was a feeling that came upon him for no reason. He just woke and thought that it was so, that this was going to be the end, the final day. He gave his last prayers and waited for it to come.

But it didn't. By noon, rain had begun dripping down from the sky in little tears, and Mr. Humpley took great comfort in thinking that the world was crying for him, and for his boy. He began pacing around in his room, which parted in the shape of an isosocles triangle. At some point, he came across a mirror and for a second saw a younger face. But the younger face fell away and his older, sadder body returned. He sighed and cried out, "Oh, my boy. Oh, my boy, where are you? God, where are you?" One of the nurses heard him and let him settle back in his bed, and she fed him. And then the man slept.

4

Mr. Humpley woke and the boy was there. The same as he always was, the same posture, the same gait, the same soul. The boy walked over to Mr. Humpley and gave him a hug. They talked. About some little things in the boy's life, some little complaint about the hospital, all about things that didn't matter, all ignoring the only thing that did matter.

At 9:00 p.m., the nurse, who was dressed in this blue-Madonna color, came and said that it was time for dinner. The boy said that he could handle it, and he, after detaching Mr. Humpley from the morphine drip, brought his dad down to the cafeteria, where they ate without words. It was lasagna, the food, and Mr. Humpley thought it was fine. In the background, people chattered. Time ticked. There was no sun.

At around 10:00, the boy began to walk Mr. Humpley back. Mr. Humpley took his time walking, and the boy stayed with him, slowing his pace. At night, the hospital lights pulsated and dripped in slow, passive globs. It looked melancholy. Eventually, while passing through the courtyard, they came upon a bench and Mr. Humpley asked to sit and the boy obliged. They sat there. The sky was above. The stars were out, dancing in this sort of milky-gray color. Birds chirruped. The boy collapsed.

"Papa, why won't you accept any treatment from the nurses? Anything, second-stage, tPA's, anything? Papa!" Mr. Humpley sighed and looked at his son, who was the only light in his life, the only star in his sky. And he smiled. And he took his boy in his arms one last time.

"My boy. My boy."

And so, the son and the father, for a moment, lay in each other's arms. Each the other's world, each the other's shadowed light.

Joey

MAX WANG, Grade 7, Age 12. Shanghai American School-Puxi Campus, Shanghai, China. Matt Errico, *Educator*

Joey snatched a slice of pizza off the untouched snack table, hesitated for the slightest fraction of a second, then hurled it across the room. Bits of cheese flew all over the gym. A few kids' eyes followed the pizza. Other kids gaped at Joey's evil grin.

"Hey!" howled a boy, picking pieces of tomato off his T-shirt. "Who threw that?"

The room slowly quieted down. Everyone glared at the boy and Joey. Suddenly, the boy grabbed an orange and attempted to throw it. The boy, not being as athletic as Joey, bungled his revenge and hit someone else. Clutching his knee, Joey tried to control his maniacal laughter. Spotting many people staring at him, he turned into a machine, rapidly blasting oranges in every direction.

After only two minutes, all the students were grabbing items and flinging them across the room. Grease dripped from walls. Sauce covered windows. Wrappers, cups, and even food-stained school bags littered the floor.

After realizing that the creator of such a horrible food fight was calmly overseeing the whole battle, a group of friends gathered around, hidden from the other kids, to discuss a plan. They wanted triumph. They wanted glory. They wanted revenge.

They sneakily slithered through the crowd like snakes chasing prey. Eyeing their target every so often, they seemed invisible inside the chaotic horde. The unsuspecting Joey never noticed them; he was busy planning another prank.

Ordering a member to go behind Joey, the determined group leader strategically started his attack. Silently, he signaled three fingers. Then two. Then one.

Seven oranges sliced through the air like knives. Seven oranges fired from strong arms like bullets from a gun. Seven oranges launched straight toward Joey like torpedoes to a ship. Impacting Joey, they exploded into sticky orange juice. Gasping as he took the attack, he didn't see the seven tomatoes coming. They exploded on contact, bursting like balloons. Desperately trying to escape, Joey slipped on a banana peel. Sore and exhausted, he raised his hand in defeat, but the attack didn't stop. In fact, even more people threw food at Joey. All the different colored splatters hitting Joey made him look like an artist's masterpiece.

And that's when they heard a loud, booming voice from behind.

A Moment of Clarity

DANIELLE GRUBER, Grade 8, Age 13. Village School, Great Neck, NY.
Lauren Sullivan, *Educator*

The symptoms started around ten years ago. In the midst of driving, Sarah's mother would forget where she was going, or she would come back panicked from the grocery store, claiming that someone had been following her. At first, her condition seemed manageable, but over time, her disorientation and confusion led to frustration and agitation, and her aggression toward others made her a concern. Sarah's decision to put her in a care center wasn't easy, but it was necessary.

Sarah tries to visit her mother every Sunday, which is when she has off from work. Some of her friends ask her how she does it—seeing her mother in that state. They ask, "Doesn't it upset you?" Sarah shrugs her shoulders and smiles sadly. "I'll always be her daughter, and I will always be there for her." This is how she avoids the question. Every time she greets her mother, expecting her dark-brown eyes to gaze at her lovingly, she is instead looked over indifferently, her mother's eyes glazed over and cold like two marbles. What Sarah really hopes for is a moment of lucidity, a moment when her mother becomes herself again.

This Sunday, her mother is pacing back and forth across her room when Sarah visits.

"Good morning," Sarah says softly. Her mother pauses momentarily and glances at Sarah, her eyebrows furrowed.

"I'm waiting for my husband," she says. Sarah's father died thirteen years ago.

"I am sure he will be here any moment," Sarah tries to say reassuringly, without her voice catching. As her mother continues to pace, Sarah cautiously heads for her unmade bed. Sometimes she gets antsy when other people touch her belongings.

But her mother is in her own world, mumbling unintelligible words under her breath and focused only on the floor in front of her. So Sarah continues on and makes her bed. She goes about the room, organizing and reorganizing the shelves, although they are filled with souvenirs from family trips, holiday cards, and other knickknacks that have lost all of their meaning. She folds her clothes and cleans the bathroom, where urine has splattered all over the floor. The cleaning personnel haven't made their rounds yet. As Sarah passes by the garbage bin, something catches her eye. It is a photograph of her mother, her father, and her standing on the beach. She sighs, cleans it off, and places it back on the dresser, even though she knows it will probably end up back in the garbage soon enough.

When there is nothing left for Sarah to clean or organize, she takes one last look around at the room, and at her mother, who is still pacing. Sarah doesn't say goodbye as she heads toward the door.

But as Sarah grasps the handle, a quavering voice whispers suddenly, "Sarah?" The word is spoken tentatively, almost as if the word, not spoken in so long, is surprising, or is refreshing on her tongue.

Sarah's body whips around. Her mother is staring right at her. And her eyes aren't glazed over. They are warm, and filled with emotion.

Tears flood Sarah's eyes and spill over as if out of an overflowing basin. She almost forgets to wrap her arms around her gently, because of her frail body. Sarah sobs and sobs, and her heaving shakes her mother's entire body. She wraps her bony arms back around Sarah and strokes her hair. She doesn't say anything, and Sarah thinks she understands.

They stand like this for what seems like forever. Sarah's tears begin to dry, and just when she finds her voice is steady enough to speak, the arms that were so lovingly wrapped around her jerk away. The lucid moment has ended.

Her mother takes a step back, looking Sarah over quizzically, probably trying to determine what she had been doing standing so close to her. But with a sigh of defeat, she shuffles back to her bed and sits down glumly.

Sarah is speechless. She feels like a gift has been presented to her and then brusquely ripped away. But she takes a deep breath and regains her composure.

"So you have a husband?" Sarah asks hesitantly, taking a step toward her mother.

"Yes, I do." Her eyes are glossy, but not like before—cold and without feeling. They seem to be in a far-off world, dreaming about something bittersweet. Sarah sits down beside her.

"Tell me about him," Sarah says, and her mother nods her head and smiles.

Six Words, One Thousand Stories

SARAH FERGUSON, Grade 11, Age 17. Riverview High School, Riverview, FL. Mike Zelazo, *Educator*

Some people hope to inspire sonnets. Others, novels. Some hope to be written as a ballad, and some would like their life to be a movie. But what if each of us got only six words?
Earth does not revolve around you.
What if your whole life was told through just six words?
Would they be good?
Old body. Young heart. Laugh lines.
Or would they be bad?
Lived sixty years, never found love.
Maybe they're haunted.
Sixteen stab wounds recorded. Died slowly.
Or maybe they speak of loss.
Pregnant wife. Alarm blaring. Never found.
Maybe as you strive for extraordinary, you find yourself with six words of truth.
Nine to five. Midlife crisis.
Maybe six words doesn't tell us anything.
Nobody knows who I am inside.
Or maybe they tell us everything.
I am a product of society.
Or maybe they tell us just enough.
Flight attendant. September 11. Final stand.
Perhaps they show just what is remembered.
Kind words. Brave actions. Great loss.

Or what is forgotten.
Pretty face. Damaged soul. Porcelain mask.
But nevertheless, they tell a story.
Firefighter. Burning house. An honorable death.
Young love. Young heart. Bad decisions.
Husband, children, dog. Life is good.
Money motivated. Love devoted. Tough choices.
Great love. Great loss. Great life.
Lived and loved together, stayed forever.
In the end, some will get sonnets and novels and movies and ballads, but others will get only six words. It is up to us what those six words say.
How will the world remember you?

The Absurd Plight of Stick-Man Steve

SAMUEL HARRIS, Grade 8, Age 13, Cloonan Middle School,
Stamford, CT. Melissa Moulketis, *Educator*

Stick-Man Steve was a living stick figure. Or maybe living wasn't quite the correct term for it (dead wasn't the correct term either)—perhaps undead? No. Stick-Man Steve was neither living, dead, nor undead. He was simply Stick-Man Steve. Because of his status as a two-dimensional entity of the homo stickapien species, Stick-Man Steve had no intestinal tract. Despite this fact, what Stick-Man Steve wanted more than anything else in the entire universe (a universe that consisted solely of ground-up wood and printed blue lines) was to eat something, specifically a sandwich. Every day, Stick-Man Steve gazed upon the sandwich that had mysteriously come into existence out of graphite two inches away from him. Stick-Man Steve, this pathetic creature that had been created on a whim with a pencil worth 5 cents during a bout of boredom, had no method of moving. Therefore, Stick-Man Steve could not reach the sandwich that was tempting him (him? her?) every day of his sad, strange little metaphorical speck of metaphorical dust that he called "life."

One day, a day that Stick-Man Steve liked to call "The Day in Which I Stare at the Same Ink Spot I Have Stared at Every Day Since I Was Born" (born? created? grown?), a loud something barreled toward Stick-Man Steve's little world, a something that proclaimed (This Narrator has no idea how Stick-Man Steve could've heard what the loud something said, for our friend Steven has no ears.):

"Notebook check, you monkeys! Get 'em out!"

God (or at least God in Stick-Man Steve's nonexistent eyes) then ripped a pencil out of a big box of pencils His mother bought for Him. God tried to erase the various doodles he had drawn in His notebook so He wouldn't get in trouble with His science teacher. What God didn't realize is that this veritable holocaust of drawings initiated a Stick-Man fight-or-flight response that suddenly allowed him to move of his own free will. Deus Stick Machina! Stick-Man Steve had gained movement! He had gained free will! Now Stick-Man Steve was truly living. He was not dead or undead, he was living! Before, Stick-Man Steve possessed a tingly shred of consciousness. But because Steve couldn't act upon his thoughts, he was not TRULY living. God wanted to kill Steve (something God couldn't do before), but one thing Stick-Man Steve wanted, nay, NEEDED before his demise at the head of an eraser was to eat a sandwich. Steve leapt across the endless chasm of paper to eat the sandwich. Stick-Man Steve ripped open his face to create a makeshift mouth, and he chomped down the entire sandwich with one bite before he was evaporated instantly by the eraser. Tragically, the sandwich tasted like nothing.

Coexisting: The Joys and Burdens of Hediyeh Azizi

SARA ZOROUFY, Grade 11, Age 16. Castilleja School, Palo Alto, CA.
Ann Wagenhals, *Educator*

House, tree, person. If I asked Hediyeh Azizi to draw these three things, it would look something like this: The sunlight in the sky would be muted by soft clouds. There would be a two-story wooden home with open windows whose curtains would blow in the wind. Through the windows you would see the brightly lit interior of the house. Next to this warm house would be an old apple tree with a dark, thick trunk. The tree would reach high into the sky above, dabbled sunlight making individual leaves glow, but its branches would sag under the weight of all the ripe apples hanging from its limbs. The person would be tall, taller than the tree and the house. Their hair would be flying in the wind, much like the curtains of the house. The person's head would be tilted toward the sky with their eyes closed, breathing in deeply. They would be standing straight, but their broad shoulders would seem heavy, as if pulling them back down from the sky. This would be Hediyeh's drawing.

The house-tree-person test, or HTP, was created by psychologist John Buck in 1948 as a tool used to "examine the subject's inner self and reveal his or her self concept and feelings about others" ("House-Tree-Person Test", Podell 40). It is an activity Hediyeh frequently uses in her work as a therapist to get to know her clients. "Art is a very powerful tool," she explains. "You can tell so much about a person from what they draw, especially for young kids who don't have the words to express how they're feeling, but they can draw it." The house is meant to give insight on the client's living condition, the tree is a reflection of the client, and the person can depict another facet of the client or their interactions with other significant people in their lives.

Her work also seems to affect her demeanor. Hediyeh has a very soft and gentle nature; when she listens to others, her eyes squint slightly and she tilts her head to the side as if she is concerned. When she speaks, she leans forward and meets the eyes of the person she's talking to. She creates a small, translucent bubble around herself and the other person and lets the rest of the bustle of the outside world become softened and blurred. This intimacy and caring personal connection that Hediyeh creates is undoubtedly a result of her work as a therapist, but there are other, more subtle signs of weariness in her behavior. When she is alone, Hediyeh always looks weighed down. Whenever she speaks about herself or the current state of the world, her lips purse and she shakes her head knowingly. She looks as though there are deep and unfortunate truths mulling in her mind, as if she has seen the reality of the world and knows its worst secrets. The worry in her eyes gives her the impression of someone who is accustomed to collecting herself and internally processing her thoughts because she has so many things she has to deal with.

Yet Hediyeh is almost unsettlingly cavalier about the emotional toll of her work. "Yes, it's really hard work," she admits, then quickly pivots before I can ask her to elaborate, "but it's very rewarding. I really like making a shift in a person's life. It's meaningful, even if it's just a small shift." I asked her several times and in several ways if the emotional burden of her work is ever too much to bear, and each time she deflects the question, turning instead to some cheerful statement. It isn't until the last few minutes of our final interview that Hediyeh opens up. "It's a lot sometimes."

Because she carries so much weight on her shoulders, Hediyeh is unwavering in her intentional practice of self-care. She walks ten miles every single day, swims, plays music, and meditates. Her activities seemed even more impressive when I realized how little time she has to fit them in: She wakes up at 6:00, meditates, and is at work by 8:00 for a staff meeting. From there she goes to an elementary school and works with three clients until 12:30. Some days, she rushes between schools in various districts. From the schools, she drives to work at the service center for rape victims until 5:30. She goes back to her office for a training meeting till 6:00 or 7:30, depending on the week. Then she takes her two-hour walk until 8:00 p.m., at which time she goes to her yoga or swimming classes until 10:30 p.m. Once she gets home and showers, she answers her work emails and calls. Some nights she is on-call with the trauma center from 7:00 p.m. to 7:00 a.m.

Despite her incredibly busy schedule, Hediyeh makes time to support herself. Hediyeh plays the daf, a traditional Iranian handheld drum with metal ringlets attached in chains to the inner rim. She explained that you just have to be with your emotions. Meditation for me is just noticing that I am feeling this way, and I'm sitting in this moment and nothing is happening, it's just all the thoughts and all the emotions, and I'm just here with them. For me, the beauty of it is that normally you have these thoughts and your body has a reaction—your heart starts beating, your chest squeezes, you can't breathe, your hands feel heavy like you just want to punch somebody—meditation lets you realize that those feelings are happening, and you just get to be with those feelings.

I was incredulous that by simply existing with your emotions, you could somehow make them less intense. How could allowing yourself to coexist with pain make the situation less painful? This was a question I grappled with for a long time while I interviewed Hediyeh, and I grew more skeptical as I learned just how intense her emotions can be.

***

It was at that moment, watching her eyes glimmer as she doubled over laughing, that I realized this joy is just as much a part of Hediyeh as the emotional burdens she carries. When she told me that meditation relaxed her because it allowed her to just be with her emotions, I was incredulous. How could relief and pain coexist? I wondered. For years I had thought that true happiness existed only in the absence of pain, but Hediyeh showed me that the two can go together. She showed me that pain doesn't have to be all-consuming, that you cannot let its weight pull you down. Hediyeh is a living example of that strength; she taught me that it is possible to carry an immense burden and still lead a truly happy life despite it. She knows that though we never may be free from worries and difficulties, pain and happiness can coexist.

Viva la Social Media

SUSAN WIE, Grade 11, Age 16. Tenafly High School, Tenafly, NJ.
Dana Maloney, *Educator*

How would the internet be described to someone who lived 200 years ago? We live in a world where "LOL" means something entirely different from "lol," where words like "Snapchat" can be used as various parts of speech, and where the number of likes on an Instagram photo equates to a certain popularity standing. In 2004, when Mark Zuckerberg created one of the most popular social media platforms to date, did he realize the monster he had birthed?

Before Instagram, Snapchat, Twitter, and even Facebook, there was AIM and MySpace. These pioneering platforms served as spaces where people could interact with others. But when did this casual use of social media become an obsession? Now, to be excluded from social media and its effects is virtually impossible. Social media has inarguably influenced our culture; unsaid rules exist and, when they are not heeded, the ghastly risk of an un-follow runs high. Instagram photos must be posted at a "prime time," Snapchat stories are not complete without the use of a geotag, and Facebook album names must border ingenious creativity. Everyone falls victim to social media—yes, even Grandma, when she participated in the renowned #MannequinChallenge this past Thanksgiving.

Social media creators are not the only ones benefiting from this phenomenon. Models Alexis Ren and Jay Alvarrez, notorious for their steamy beachside Instagram photos and adventurous YouTube videos, have 7.1 million and 4.7 million followers on Instagram, respectively. Their infamous adventures to Greece and Tahiti, among other exotic locations, led to the debuts of both models in music videos, car commercials, and photo shoots. Not only did the broadcasting of their lives lead to greater opportunities, they were also paid by airline companies to travel and publicize their exciting lifestyle.

So in the age of flourishing Instagram models and money deposits through Snapchat, the world around us is truly becoming a place distinctly different from that of our grandparents. Rather, social media now serves as a platform where people can involve themselves in the political realm.

Throughout this past presidential election race, many people argue, the only real winner was the media. The media's presence certainly added to the colossal amount of misinformation during this election. For example, Trump's planned policy regarding the deportation of immigrants was highly reliant on the widely accepted theory that Mexican immigrants are stealing American jobs. However, reliable sources such as *The New York Times, Forbes, The Atlantic,* and the Huffington Post have published articles stating that this notion is not true.

In addition to Trump's policies being accepted by many because of this kind of misinformation, the way in which people reacted to his win as the president-elect was also jaded by misinformation. In retrospect, many people claim that Donald Trump's victory was not statistically surprising but only alarmed people because of his portrayal as the laughingstock of the political sphere. Nate Silver of fivethirtyeight.com wrote on November 1, "In fact, Clinton would probably lose the electoral college in the event of a very close national popular vote." Based on poll results, the idea of Donald Trump winning was not impossible. But as the abundance of Donald Trump memes and comedic remixes of his speeches were constantly shared on Facebook, the public viewed him as more of a buffoon than a candidate, resulting in the shock that followed his win. In addition to social media's impact on national affairs, international events are also affected by social media's takeover.

Many hate our generation's growing dependency on social media, and technology in general, but no one can deny its potential to impact humanity in powerful ways, including for rebellion. In 2010 and 2011, angry Tunisians protested against a repressive government. However, civil unrest truly broke out in December 2010, when Mohamed Bouazizi, a Tunisian street vendor, set himself on fire. This act was a clear expression of the despondency many Tunisians felt from the dictatorial rule of the government. As the video of Bouazizi took to Twitter and Facebook, Bouazizi's actions inspired many and riots began to spread as a symbol of unity against the government.

Social media affects the many aspects that compose our culture and the world we live in. Instead of Polaroid photography, there is the Snapchat camera. Instead of writing letters, there is the ability to tweet at someone. Instead of sharing CDs and records, there is Spotify, where collaborative playlists allow people to share music. In our world, virtually nothing is the same as it was even twenty years ago. The social media revolution is real, and it is now.

IO PERL-STRAHAN, ***Nina***, Grade 10, Age 15, Hunter College High School, New York, NY. Constance Rich, *Educator*

The Matriarchy

CAROLINE COOK, Grade 12, Age 17. Sanford School, Hockessin, DE.
Brianna Smale, *Educator*

After an eternity passed and I survived what must've been four heart attacks, the President appeared. She was a young woman, tall and willowy, looking like a forceful wind could've swept her away: not really the strong, intense presence I was anticipating. She had shoulder-length black hair, straight and smooth, and the same serious eyes I recognized on Emma. Her head spun around her neck like an owl's; those glassy gray eyes followed you and stared straight into your soul. The President was up for re-election, and she'd been on the defensive for months. I could see the exhaustion that months of campaigning had pressed into her taut, thin face.

Isaiah had encouraged me to take an interest in politics, even though neither of us were able to vote, and I had read about this woman so many times I barely believed she was real. It was like sighting a dragon, majestic and terrifying. I nearly expected her to breathe fire.

A team of dutiful shadows followed her, spreading the speech on the podium, filling a glass of water, holding an umbrella to shade her skin—paper-white like the marble of the Capitol—from the harsh sun. It was bright that day, like the sun itself didn't want the Earth to hide in the shadows anymore. I squinted to catch every detail. I knew I was going to remember this moment. The President was going to speak about Isaiah, my Isaiah, and he couldn't be there to see it. I had to remember everything for him.

***

The whole world stopped spinning for that one moment. I closed my eyes and finally heard those sweet words that Isaiah had told me with confidence that neither of us would ever hear.

"Boys will now be allowed in schools."

Then everything went black.

***

I had fainted.

When I awoke, Isaiah stood above me, beaming with his rare smile. I was in my bed, cushioned by pillows and bags of ice. There was the dull presence of pain whispering in all of my joints, but despite the cold compresses, I was filled with warmth. What was this feeling, stretching through my chest? Flowers were blooming, a fire was lit. Warmth, when I looked at him. I looked at him and my eyes ached from trying to see him, soaking up every detail, all at once. Isaiah. Here, with me. He sat down at the foot of the bed, and I watched as his eyes wandered the room, tracing every object. The leg of a table. The pile of laundry. My face. They lingered there.

I propped myself up on my elbow, which had been bandaged, though I didn't remember why. "What are you doing?"

"Looking at your room." He smiled and exhaled peaceful air. "I missed this house."

He filled me in on all that I'd missed. Apparently my fainting in the street upon hearing the good news came at the most inopportune time. Almost immediately after the address, riots broke out in the street, both for and against the President's rather sudden and unprecedented decision, and I got trampled underfoot. I had been asleep for three days, bruised and battered, and when I awoke, the world had become a very different place.

I had slept through the revolution.

Isaiah was personally released from prison by the President—the image I'd conjured of her unlocking his cell door would remain tattooed in my mind forever—and had returned to work at our house hours later. He told me about the walk out of the prison: crowds of screaming reporters, documenting everything. People there to support him, people there to fight him, people there just to see him. People, filling the streets. People to see Isaiah.

The world hadn't slept since the news broke, and the city itself lay in pieces. Angry businesswomen and members of high society, floored by the groundbreaking turn of events, had set fire to buildings and defaced the Capitol. Broken windows, shattered glass, rubble, and even blood. All of this, just for some books?

Protests these were not; violence, anger, a manifestation of the ugly and the raw was all that we saw. The President hadn't been seen since the address, and many men (especially Isaiah) hadn't dared go outside. Rumors flew about women attacking any man carrying a book or even a newspaper—though they were legal then—fearing that he had helped in the "revolution." Men went missing, men we knew. Boys, only children. The police suspected murder. The all-women police force, mad with power and high on estrogen, weren't motivated to calm the riots. Many took part in the attacks on literate men. Needless to say, we weren't expecting the police to pursue any murder cases.

***

Isaiah and I made it to the school after ducking and kicking and dropping our books and running for our lives. We were chased all the way to the school doors. He threw them open and made sure I was inside first.

In the longest minutes that followed, I sat on the cold floor of the lobby, eyes fixed on the door, panting like a dog. Isaiah had blockaded the door, watching through the crack to see when more of our own had made it to safety. The door was forced open and more boys crawled through, clothes torn, blood on their arms, dirt on their faces, and books, beloved books, nowhere to be seen.

Those moments were little eternities. The shouting outside was making me dizzy. Bricks were thrown through the windows of the school, shattered glass skittering across the floor. Notes tied to the projectiles threatened a continued violence if boys were still allowed in the school. Isaiah collapsed onto the floor suddenly, weeping. This emotional—uniquely male—behavior that was once a chink in the armor of our fearless leader was now a weekly routine; his endless energy was beginning to be taxed by the crush of society. I forced myself to look away from his figure, beautiful and tragic, draped on the floor.

The girls had all made it safely inside, but no one ever went to class. That day we all just huddled in the lobby, afraid to move, listening to the strange and horrible noises from outside. We all held hands. The girls sat with us in our vigil.

***

All of the air was sucked out of that room, and it seemed like everyone stopped breathing. Never have I been in a space so quiet. It wasn't just silent; it was the absence of silence. A vacuum. I could hear the blood in my ears, the pulse sounded like a drum.

I looked around me at the sea of black fabric and tear-stained faces. The men had their heads bowed, salty eyes staring at their shoes, their lips moving in silent prayer or pressed tight into a hard line to keep the emotion firmly inside. The men all looked the same, they all felt the same hurt. It was the women who stood out. Their eyes were fixed on Isaiah, his body shaking on the podium, and they all seemed to be leaning toward him like magnets in a painful empathy. I could tell that they all felt his pain, they all understood the rock that replaced my heart, it would never be quite the same. It took Matthew's death to make them understand.

I couldn't tear my eyes away from Isaiah's figure on the humble wooden podium that was too small to support the weight of the day. Isaiah, too, was too small to support the weight of the day.

The world was watching, and they couldn't ignore what they had done.

The Sky at 5 a.m.

LIAM SWIFT, Grade 10, Age 16. Casco Bay High School, Portland, ME.
Molly McGrath, *Educator*

Prologue

I have almost memorized the pattern made by the cracks on the ceiling above my bed. I have only been in this house for a month. The cracks are thin and wiry; cracks that spiral across the white paint. The ceiling is safe and sturdy, even though the cracks still sometimes haunt me when the sun goes down. Nightmares used to come about the world unraveling and the attic crashing through. The cracks stay, etched in my vision when I close my eyes before falling asleep and there again when I open them in the morning. When night falls, the headlights of cars shine through the slats of my window shade and beam to the ceiling before disappearing once more. In the first week, I would stay up looking at them, looking at the way the light touched only slivers of the ceiling as it made its way through my venetian blinds. I would stay up, sometimes even all night until morning would approach, silently as morning often does. At these times, the night, this unseen creature, would seem more like a friend than an enemy. My ceiling was a universe, one where you could see all the imperfections in the perfect-looking night sky. Staying awake and imagining this would keep the nightmares from coming. The nightmares don't come that often anymore, even though it's only been four weeks since we moved in. But the cracks still peer at me with the brimming nervousness of their existence. Seven cracks. Seven faults.

This August, my mother quit her counseling job in Nashville for a well-paying health care job in the town of Greyson, Arkansas, population 52,000. Not exactly the most exciting place. I have been to Greyson only a couple of times to visit my grandpa, but there's not much about the town itself that sticks in my mind. My visits to my grandpa were leisurely yet tiring. I used to dread these trips, not because I don't like my grandpa, but because there was absolutely nothing to do. He lives in a rented house on the edge of town, in a place called Five Corners, out where it looks more like country than city. The nearest neighbor is down the road a ways, and in this case it was a guy who I am supposedly related to but am not sure exactly how. We rarely saw him on these childhood trips—he just stayed in his house down the road. When we did see him, it was just to pop in and check on the house or something, but not really to visit us.

My whole family is from Greyson, including my dad, who grew up here as a child. We would never explore the town, which was what I was most interested in. The house was stuffy and beige, and Grandpa, in his white dress shirt, bolo string tie, and wire-rim glasses, would just talk about the weather and what the president was doing wrong. The only thing I would look forward to on these visits was Grandpa's big front lawn, though my parents wouldn't let me go out to play there much. "Socialize," my mom would tell me, with widening eyes, giving me the do-what-I-say look. Mom would be caring for my little sister, and I would just sit around with them, bored. And Dad, he would have sophisticated-looking chats with his dad. That was before he left.

We paid another visit to my grandpa right after we moved here. Mom, feeling tired of our routined life in Nashville, found a new job and a newly developed subdivision and suddenly I found myself here. Grandpa welcomed us in for a couple of days, looking exactly the same as I remember him. It was just like the old visits, minus Dad.

I turned seventeen last February, and I am going to be a junior at Alum Brook High School this September. Greenlinks, where we moved in, is a flat little Greyson subdivision consisting of a couple of one- or two-story buildings in the downtown area. These buildings consist of the Greenlinks Convenience Store, which has been boarded up since I arrived here, a Shell gas station with a food mart whose signature and only dish is a Dixie cup filled with over-fried potatoes you have to press the grease out of. And 32 miles outside of Greenlinks lies the monstrosity of Alum Brook, my new high school.

Alum Brook is a large boarding school with a campus full of clad-roofed buildings protected by an orchard of pines with a wooden sign displaying its name that squeaks in even the slightest wind. This massive school is where all the wealthy parents in Little Rock send their kids. Given the situation that Alum Brook is only 32 miles away and costs money, and Greenlinks High School is a couple of blocks away and is free, I'm assuming my sister and I will be among the only Alum Brook students from this area. This inconvenience may mean limited friend options, given the fact that we couldn't hang out on the weekends when I will be back home. We figured out that, because of the 32-mile difference, we'll be staying in dorms there and coming home on the weekend. Clover and I mutually agreed we would want the boarding school over the public school. "I want an adventure," I told Mom, Clover nodding along behind me but without speaking. We decided I would be the speaker, because I am better at convincing. Mom said no at first, but once I brought up the moving and how painful it was for us, she gave in. Little Rock, where most Alum kids live, is almost three hours away from Greyson. And, obviously, there is no such brook as "Alum Brook." Surrounding the Shell are some newish houses that make up the subdivision. There's not much difference between the two-story Greenlinks houses except every other one is flipped around, mirroring the one next to it. And they are all painted with washed-out colors, such as dirt brown, earthworm pink, and camo green. It's probably the ugliest subdivision in Greenlinks, and they can get pretty ugly. One of the better subdivisions in Greyson that Clover and I were rooting for is called Coral Hills, which is a group of big, fat, chihuahua-like McMansions. But the persuading didn't go through on this one. The guy at the Shell told me you should avoid Coral Hills, so I do. This is the whole world and system of Greyson, isolated within the edges of the city, but beyond that, it's mines. Beyond those, the farms. Beyond those, just hills. Rocks, dust, and hills.

My name is Kyle Sanders, and I wouldn't say there is much that is special about me. I have a mop of dark hair and brown eyes. I'm a bit unextraordinary, despite the fact that I have an unusual love for music. Maybe it's because I spent a large portion of my life in Nashville. I usually like to listen to vinyl, because my dad gave me his collection at a young age. It was mostly filled with oldies (and surprisingly not much country, given that we lived in Nashville), but I began to appreciate music then. There was a song called "Josephine" by this old band that I would listen to on repeat in my bedroom when I was nine after my dad was called back to active duty in the Navy SEALs. I lost a few records, including "Josephine," because of an uncontrolled stove fire in the Nashville house. We (myself, my mom, and my sister, Clover) were all safe, but my closest companion, my records, were not. Only a few of them survived the fire, and since then I've been building up the collection to what it used to be. I have to admit, it's pretty easy to find vinyl in Nashville. But I'm not in Nashville anymore. That's the problem. I'm in the middle of nowhere in a flat town with flat people. Greyson's industry is coal mining. The city sells the coal to the furnace companies, and it gets money, which gets deposited into the banks downtown. It all works like a well-oiled machine. The way I see it, the downtown is the heart; it keeps the city alive. The streets are the veins, they bind the city and transport things from one place to another. The houses and subdivisions are the cells; they're what the city is made up of. And the people, they're the blood. They oil the gears. Without them, the machine will eventually rust and break down. Just like everything does sooner or later. Even us.

To Walk On

DANIEL BLOKH, Grade 10, Age 15. Alabama School of Fine Arts, Birmingham, AL. Ashley Jones, *Educator*

My maternal grandmother is called Babushka. It is a soft and beautiful name, translating to the formal grandmother in English, a word that parts easily from the lips, that brings curious Americans asking us what the word means. Svetlana, my father's mother, becomes Baba Sveta. A word that is quicker, harsher. Brisk.

***

My father is not an angry man. He has yelled at my mother a few times, but he feels guilty immediately, as he makes known by apologizing a hundred times. One conversation, however, never fails to rile him up.

"I saw your mom on the bench today. She spoke to me with such a tortured voice."

"What did she say?" my father asks, his voice hushed. I listen to them from another room, working on a math sheet for school.

"I asked her why she was just sitting there," my mother says, "and she said, 'Oh, Ritochka, my legs hurt so bad. I just cannot walk today.'"

"She's being lazy," my father says. "As usual."

"You should make her be active. Or go on a walk with her." I lay my pencil down as I listen to them, waiting for the voices to rise.

"I've tried to, all right? You think I haven't tried? She complains about her arthritis and her pinched nerve and refuses to do anything."

"Well, this won't do her any good. The more she sits, the more untrained her muscles will get. At this pace, she'll never walk."

"I don't know what to do! She refuses to walk. She won't listen to me. What should I do, force her to move?"

And so the voices build on and on, until the conversation snaps closed with a shout, and my father walks around with a throat full of apology until the day my mother brings up the subject again.

***

As the youngest child in my family, I am used to being treated more carefully than my siblings. I am the second chance, my father's opportunity to teach a child how to drive without making them cry, my brother's shot at treating a sibling kindly for a change. I can't say I mind.

Among my family, Baba Sveta has stood out. All through the years, she has been unusually nice to me. The usual treatment of my siblings was to scold them, take offense over tiny matters, and make unkind remarks behind their backs. Matters between her and my mother have been complicated, and her idea of a phone conversation with my father is a shouting match. But for me, she always smiles and talks nicely, spares twenty dollars as a birthday present, leaves cookies out on her table when she knows I will visit. I'm not sure why, but still, I can't say I mind.

***

Both of my grandparents call our house every night, often around the same time. Babushka, at 86, calls because she has suddenly forgotten where she is, because she doesn't know where my late grandfather has gone, because our number is written above her bed for situations like this. Baba Sveta, at 78, calls to complain about her legs.

When the calls come, I am often in bed, pretending to sleep as I read by flashlight.

"I told you not to call me at this hour," my father will say, his voice as warlike as a bellow with the volume turned down. "What am I supposed to do about your legs, Mom? Drive over here now, at nine in the evening? No, I expect you to act like a grown woman, not a child!" By the time the conversation comes to a close, my father's voice is just a normal bellow. "No, and if you call me again, I'm not coming to your house tomorrow. Goodnight."

I can even hear Baba Sveta's voice screaming from the phone as my father pulls it from his ear and slams it down. "I don't know what to do," he will shout into the silence, as though Baba Sveta is still present there somehow, ready to ask him again to bring a new box of chocolate cereal. There is only the quiet house, listening.

***

One evening, while my father is asleep and my mother is gone grocery shopping, Baba Sveta calls. By the time I pick up, she is already in mid-sentence, her voice half tearful and half a barbaric cry.

". . . sleep and can't stand it hurts so bad. What did your poor mother do to deserve this from her own son?"

"Baba Sveta, this is your grands—"

"I can't stand this arthritis, and you barely . . . " She stops in her tracks in sudden realization. "Oh, grandson, is that you?" she says, her voice suddenly sweet and melodic. "So nice to hear you! Grandson, could you please pass the phone to your father for me?"

***

Baba Sveta is a controversial subject. When talking to her, my father yells and bellows, punctuates sentences with the slamming of a phone. And yet, when he talks about her, my father is gentle. "I know I shouldn't bring this," my father says before driving over to her house with a newly requested soda. "But what can I do? She's my mother, and she's in a lot of pain."

***

As the years go on, Baba Sveta starts to call more often. Two times a night, then three. The arthritis in her legs gets worse. She stops taking the elevator ride to sit on the bench outside and retires to her apartment, which slowly attracts roaches because of her lack of cleaning. My father decides he cannot take it anymore. He threatens to take her to the ER if she calls again. She calls again.

"I don't know if it will help," he says before leaving. "But it's the only thing I can do. Maybe they'll operate on her again." Baba Sveta had a joint surgery less than two years ago, which did little good for her, but suspended her pain for a few months.

If they decide to operate on her leg again, he tells me with a hopeful voice, perhaps she could get on her feet, perhaps even get out of her room again, but I know the most he is hoping for is that she lets him sleep.

***

My father has to be at the hospital on the day of the joint surgery, so my mother drives me to school and back. She tells me that Baba Sveta knows enough English to get through it, but my father is mostly there to keep her from upsetting a doctor.

"She's never been pleasant with strangers," my mother says. "Once, she was stopped at a grocery store because she walked out with a few items. She didn't know the language well enough to communicate fluently, but enough to shout at them and throw a fit when they tried to stop her. They ended up letting her go because they didn't want to deal with her." She sighs. "Well, I guess it worked."

***

When my father picks me up from school the following day, I say hello, then pull out my homework for the day and begin to work. We ride silently for a few minutes.

"You know, you haven't even asked about Baba Sveta," my father says eventually. "Did you forget she was just in the ER?"

"Mom told me she was all right this morning, so I didn't ask," I say. Truthfully, amidst last night's history homework and the commonness of Baba Sveta's uneventful health scares and visits to various doctors, I had forgotten. "I'm sorry." I pause. "How is she?"

"She's fine. She went home today," my father says.

"Did the doctor tell you if there's anything he could do to help?" I ask.

"Not really," my father says. "He prescribed some stronger medications."

***

During lunch that day, I take a walk. The wind pushes against me, whistles past my ears and lifts my jacket. I feel my legs beneath me, strong, so strong they push me past the wind again and again. I try to imagine pain in them, to add it into the skin and bone and muscle like a spice. I try to imagine what I will become with age.

But I am fifteen. I am not old, and I cannot conjure the experience of senility, cannot make myself suffer. Each leg moves forward freely, raises, settles into the dirt, pushes forward. I cannot make myself blow over in the wind.

***

The next time I visit Babushka, we invite Baba Sveta over. They live in the same apartment complex, though several floors away from one another. We expect her not to come, but she does. To our surprise, she walks in smiling. In the past, she often gave me quick, half-hearted grins when I saw her, but this time, she holds the sunny face for one minute, two, even three. A world record.

"Oh, grandson, how are you doing?" she asks. Her face looks artificial, painted on. "I love you so very much. You know that, right?"

My mother meets my eyes, both of us equally confounded.

"How are you?" I ask, turning to Baba Sveta. Her eyes stare past me for a few seconds before slowly coming to focus on me, as though I were a specter slowly materializing before her.

"I'm sorry, grandson. What'd you ask?"

"How are you doing?"

"Oh, wonderful," she says. And again, her eyes begin to drift past me. I walk to my mother.

"It must be from the new medicine," my mother remarks. "She came all the way here without complaining about her legs." She shakes her head. "Well, your father didn't have much of a choice."

Later that day, all four of us go walking.

***

Each time I meet her after that, she seems even more happy, more dazed. More medicated. She wears a smile from ear to ear. We go on walks with the whole family, strolling in the warm summer air. Slowly but surely, she stops calling my father as often.

"She's really improved," my mother tells my father. "She seems happy. And I think she's put on weight."

"Yes, I agree," my father says, and his voice does not rise.

***

A few weeks later, I am walking down the road, and I spot Baba Sveta across from me. She is walking toward me, pushing her walker along in front of her. The warm summer sun illuminates her and she smiles, a smile wider than I've ever seen before. I am scared. Her mouth does not open to call my name, to tell me to walk with her. In those eyes, full of a dangerous bliss, no recognition of me. But I should not weep or worry, right? It shouldn't matter. She can walk now, and I should be so proud of her, and her legs are so strong—look at them—so strong they push her right past me.

Black Lives Matter

MEGAN GONZALEZ, Grade 12, Age 18. Durant High School, Plant City, FL.
Laura Estes-Swilley and Holley Kimble, *Educators*

Equality should be easy enough to understand. It is the idea that every man, woman, and child are equal. My parents always taught me that everyone on this Earth is equal in the eyes of God, and that every life has value. Growing up Mexican-American, I have faced derogatory comments from my peers about my race, which has made me feel less than equal. These comments only further solidified my belief that everyone should be treated the same, no matter where they come from. Over recent months, there has been social unrest, with racial campaigns rising across the United States. The Black Lives Matter campaign specifically struck a chord in my belief that all lives are equal. Upon first hearing about it, I thought that it was the African-American community claiming that their lives held more value than other lives—Asian, Hispanic, Native American, and White. I felt as if this ever-growing debate was challenging my long-cherished belief. I have since learned that this is not the case.

The three words Black Lives Matter mean many different things to many different people. When I first heard of this campaign, it was explained to me that the African-American community was arguing that their lives were more important than the other millions of lives in America. I immediately felt negatively toward this campaign, and it upset me that so many people supported this argument. As the riots became more frequent, so did the publicity covering the cause. Instead of closing myself off, I listened to what people had to say about it. In doing this, I learned so much about not only the cause, but also about America as a broken nation. I learned that Black Lives Matter is not the belief that only black lives matter, it's the belief that black lives matter too. This difference may seem insignificant, but really it spoke volumes about the way black lives have been treated in America. Throughout history in America, all minorities, not just African-Americans, have faced discrimination and hardship simply because of what they look like. But to deny that African-Americans have significant barriers to overcome based on their skin color is denying American history, such as slavery, Jim Crow laws, and the civil rights movement. The purpose of this cause is to call attention to the struggles African-Americans must face, the struggles that white people simply cannot understand. Black Lives Matter is reminding the American people that African-Americans, who have been continually treated as if their lives hold less value, should be given the same opportunities, and should be treated the same as their white neighbors. In retaliation to this campaign came "All Lives Matter." American people not of the African-American community felt like they were being told their lives were unimportant and devalued. They stood up in protest, saying "all lives matter," but this was never the case that African-Americans were trying to make. The problem in America isn't that all lives were being discriminated against; it was that African-American lives and minorities' lives were being discriminated against. Every time someone shouts that "all lives matter," they are missing the point. They are choosing not to see the racism that still exists today, and they are putting up more barriers for black people in America to overcome.

As long as groups are still struggling because of their race, religion, or any other reason, there will never truly be equality. I hope that as a nation we push forward to this goal of equality, because I fear an America where we send refugees back to their warring nations. I fear an America where we build a wall to keep out migrants who are trying to create a new life. I fear an America where Muslims cannot practice their religion in peace. It may at times seem like equality will never be achieved, and recently it's felt like America has gone backwards in our battle against inequality. But we can make new strides toward equality. Some are leaps, like the legalization of gay marriage. Some are a single step, like the Black Lives Matter movement. Just because we do not work in a courthouse or live in the White House does not mean that we cannot effect change as a nation. We will one day have the equality that Thomas Jefferson promised us so many years ago. But we must start new movements that make people think about what is happening around them, and we must support old movements that still hold truth. Because the day that we fall silent is the day that injustice wins. So keep protesting, and keep questioning, because one day our efforts will lead to an America where inequality is a thing only read about in textbooks.

Believe

JAHYDE BULLARD, Grade 12, Age 17. Vermont Academy,
Saxtons River, VT. Joanne Fuller, *Educator*

I am considered lucky. Developing a great relationship with my teacher and mentor, Lisa Ryan, I was able to get an experience that most people in Camden didn't. I traveled to Vermont with Lisa the summer after fourth grade. The drive, which felt like the longest ride ever, was worth it because it helped motivate me and shape the person I am today.

After a long six hours, I remember seeing a sign that read, "Welcome to Vermont." I stuck my head out of the window and began breathing in as hard as I could. I had never smelled air that was so fresh, and so filled with the smell of beautiful flowers and happiness. I was amazed by the overly tall trees and the signs that said "Moose Crossing." What caught my eye the most were the huge houses that had driveways and big yards with the greenest grass my eyes had ever seen. Throughout the week I stayed in Vermont, I had many first-time experiences. These included my first hike, my first lobster, my first time driving a mower, and most of all, my first time believing.

My dad was killed the spring prior to this trip in a drive-by shooting. My dad was my role model, and many people began to worry about me after his death, especially Lisa. My mom was still alive, but she was at one of two places, back in jail or on her corner selling dope. Either way, she wasn't in my life. My story was the same as that of most kids in Camden, poor with no parents to look up to. Why would I believe? I had no reason to, until Lisa gave me the opportunity to do so.

Camden, New Jersey, is a place where most people don't believe. They don't believe in education. They don't believe in success. Unfortunately, it is not their fault. The people develop this attitude by what they are surrounded by every day. They see nonstop poverty, violence, and drug dealing. They watch parents struggle to get jobs. How could they believe? By believe, I mean having the strength to want to do better, as both a person and in life. Most don't have the opportunity to see the world and have experiences beyond the city of Camden. For example, before attending my eighth-grade graduation in Vermont, my grandma had never left the state of New Jersey. You could tell from her body language that she was in complete culture shock.

After the trip to Vermont, I had my mind set on one thing and one thing only, and that was to get out of Camden, New Jersey. I saw that life was so much more than what Camden offered me. That trip gave me the hope and strength to strive for more than drug dealing and a one-bedroom apartment. Shortly after the trip, I decided that I wanted to leave Camden and attend a boarding school in Vermont. That is when I was accepted to Kurn Hattin Homes at the beginning of my fifth-grade year. I have now officially been in the state of Vermont for seven years, and I will soon be the first person in my family to graduate from high school. Yes, I miss my family daily, and unfortunately, even the streets of Camden. But I know in the long run that by leaving I am helping my family, and giving other people in Camden the hope to make it out.

My grandma reminds me often of how proud she is of who I have become. I use her words as motivation to do even better. I want nothing more than the best for my family and the city that raised me. I don't ever see myself going back, but instead using my story to motivate others in Camden to do better. I can't thank Lisa enough for giving me the opportunity to believe.

Sonata No. 2

DAVID HOU, Grade 11, Age 16. Adlai E. Stevenson High School, Lincolnshire, IL. Dawn Forde, *Educator*

I. Exposition

A broken coffee machine, unwashed dishes, dirty floors. It's the little things that spark the sudden, divisive arguments. Dirt has crept its way into the crevices of the once-shiny wooden panels; dust has settled onto countertops and shelves in each room; old slippers, used socks, and unopened mail rest undisturbed, cluttered throughout the ground and carpet.

I've always considered my mom to be a slight germaphobe, and every day she seemingly discovers a new bacteria-infested, dusty, unsanitary item to gripe about. My dad's lackluster cleaning ability or, in other words, laziness, only heightens the tensions between the two. On the weekdays, he drops me off at school, drives to work, grumpily drags his weary baggage home, and moseys into his room. From there, he appears to never leave his isolated paradise, claiming that he needs to "work on his computer." Now repeat this monotonous cycle, with the clock only winding down for my mom to explode.

Then it happens late into the night. I hear yelling from opposite sides of the house in a mixture of phrases in both English and Chinese; complaints and criticisms of each other's mannerisms and habits are shot back and forth.

And a few days later, the house would somehow be clean, silent, and harmonious.

Tick.

"Sonata form is composed in three parts—an exposition, a development, and a recapitulation," Mr. Ernst reminded us again, as he adjusted his round, thick-rimmed spectacles. "The exposition, essentially, states the main themes of the piece, setting the building blocks for the remainder of the composition." We silently observed as he strolled around the room, running his long fingers through his coarse, gray hair. Then my eyes slowly drifted to the long second hand of the analog clock, shifting rhythmically with the passage of time. I began counting the number of minutes left: one, two, three . . .

Tock.

. . . four.

I turn off the metronome, staring blankly at the sheet music. The deep, black eyes of the notes stare right back. Frustrated, I rest my head on the jumble of dark ink that forms symbols, lines, and numbers that somehow make sense to me. Slow and consistent practice, I tell myself. Right hand alone. Slow and consistent practice. Left hand alone. Slow and consistent practice. Both hands together. Slow and consistent—

"Andy! Tell your dad to wash the dishes!"

I'll Take a Little Bit of Everything

ABEY PHILIP, Grade 11, Age 17. duPont Manual High School, Louisville, KY. Alesia Williams, *Educator*

I love food. You could call me a foodie, if you prefer. I just call it human. I love all food—any shape, color, texture, or flavor—I don't discriminate. My plate can be filled with anything: latkes, paneer makhani, naan, grits, pastitsio, grape leaves, and much more. I'm the person in the buffet line who takes a little bit of everything. The person with the multicolored and multicultural plate equipped with a smorgasbord of varying flavors. Not only is my plate diverse, but I am as well.

I was born on a rainy September day in the province of Andhra Pradesh, in a small town called Bhilai, to a twenty-five-year-old newly divorced woman I call my mother. This seems simple enough. Wrong. The events culminating in my birth were anything but simple.

My story does not begin on September 13, 1999, in Bhilai, India. My story starts in the year 586 BCE in Jerusalem, Israel. My story is the story of my ancestors. In the year 586 BCE, on the tenth day of the tenth month, Babylonian king

Nebuchadnezzar marched his army against Jerusalem and laid siege upon the city. The grand temple of Solomon, framed with prime quarried stone and exotic cedar wood, reaching a height of more than twenty stories, was set ablaze and burned to the ground. During the siege, my ancestors fled from the burning Israel and took refuge in southern India, in a province now known as Kerala.

Flash forward five hundred years to the year of our lord 52 AD. Before his ascension, Jesus asked his disciples to spread the gospel to all the people of all the nations in all the tongues of man. The Apostle Thomas gave credence to this call of action and decided to spread the good news of the gospel to his Jewish brethren who had lived in southern India since the fall of the First Temple of Solomon. His journey resulted in the conversion of my ancestors and many others, which made them some of Christianity's earliest converts.

While the religion may be new, the traditions are old. We cover our heads during worship; our communion is called Qurbana, which is Aramaic for sacrifice; our cross is called the nasrani menorah because it sits atop a seven-branched lamp stand. Another tradition we hold is giving our children Hebrew names. My first name, for example, is Abey, which is Hebrew for Abraham. My family and I have practiced Eastern Orthodox Christianity for about two thousand years; one could say it is another one of our traditions.

Kerala, India, is a unique locale because of the great diversity it embodies: Hindus, Muslims, Jews, Buddhists, and Christians have lived in relative harmony for thousands of years. I have direct ties to both Christianity and Judaism, but in addition I feel a strong connection to Islam and Hinduism because of the aforementioned diversity. If my parents had been born five hundred feet to their left, they would have been born into a Muslim household; if they were born five hundred feet to their right, then they would have been born into a Hindu household. The connection I feel with this assortment of religions has shaped me into the person I am today. It made me realize that it does not matter what religion one is born into or chooses, because in the end, under all the hijabs, crosses, and yarmulkes, we all share 99.5 percent of the same DNA, and we all share this beloved planet.

Flash forward again, back to 1999. It was the thirteenth of September, and the monsoon season was coming to an end; however, on that day, it was not. The rain was pouring, gushing down the drainpipes, and flooding the streets of Bhilai. It is 9:00 in the morning, my mother is in labor at Apollo Hospital, and about a mile down the road, an elderly, five-foot-nine gray-haired man is running toward the hospital to see his first grandson. The clock strikes five past ten, and the nurse is scribbling down the odd Hebrew name of the screaming child in my mother's arms—the same arms I will be held in on our voyage to America a year and a half later. I was born into a poor family in a poor town in a poor country. I was, however, rich in one respect: my heritage. That is my badge of honor and my pride.

A year and a half later, my family and I were able to come to America to live the American Dream: Get fat and get rich. We first stepped foot on American soil in the great state of New Jersey, so that means before the era of Chris Christie. We first stepped foot on this vast frontier of opportunity with one hundred dollars and two suitcases among the four of us: my mom, my grandparents, and myself. I do not remember too much of the Garden State, but I do remember how happy I was when my mom told me we were moving to Kentucky. Moving to the state of barefoot hicks was the best news I had ever heard. Louisville is now my home; Kentucky is my home; America is my home.

Peel

KELLEY LIU, Grade 11, Age 16. Troy High School, Troy, MI.
Valerie Valentino, *Educator*

Every day I peel something without purpose, not because it's compulsion, but because we're always peeling things without noticing. Oranges, bananas, apples, plastic wrap, expiration stickers, aluminum foil. If the skin or wrapping tears unevenly, it's a bad omen, and my fingernails become stained with blotched juice for the rest of the day. This morning it's a hard-boiled egg—the whites peek out, naked and wholesome under shed skin.

The plastic tree was only $49. It stands next to another fake plant, something that could have been perennial. Sometimes I think the tree admires winter more than I do, staring loudly out the living room window. Its tinsel and bells are stitched onto its branches, but we've never put it away to notice.

My mother's packages sit expectantly on the front steps when I get home, as though they might let themselves in. Their mailing stickers still put her address as ours. I peel the stickers off and roll them in my hands, the adhesive pulling gently on the skin of my palm.

My friend texts me about a show I should watch, one of the many recommendations he's given. We share a connection in gender that makes the friendship seem more intimate than it is. I think about my inability to provide things for him, my inability to contribute anything meaningful. I ignore his message and wonder how I have so little to do.

Every time it snows, the cars push a muddy line of slush through the road that runs near our backyard. The soiled landscape is like a painting torn up by teeth, white dirtied by tobacco or chocolate. The chiaroscuro of branches, hills, people. The headlights erratic through the trees.

My mother still calls sometimes to inquire after the state of things. Have you been eating well? Has it been too long since we've talked?

Over the weekend I acquire a hangnail. It gets caught on a belt loop as I get dressed. I peel it back enough to use scissors, but I accidentally nip off a piece of flesh.

The seams of my backpack are still intact. It's the zipper that's broken. My friend was the first to notice. I have to be wary of carrying too much weight or the zipper will pop open like stitches on the forearm of some great beast, rippling under strain and contortion.

I've found an outlet in sketching the boundaries of objects, enclosing them in dark lines. Their outlines overlap in charcoal to make thick strokes, dense and tangled. The white shines through the cracks.

My friend waves in the crowded hallway and walks over, looking out of place. His curls, mottled skin, and pink cuticles are thick, like eraser shavings that bunch up in the middle of the page. He tells me about a new friend he's made—they're on the debate team together. I smile and pick at my hangnail as he blends in with the crowd.

My curtain is hardly a curtain; it's a silk bedsheet, yellowing, and thick enough to mute midday but thin enough to let mornings in. At night, tree branches flash shadows on the pale canvas as cars turn into the road behind our house, their headlights blinding.

I try to pick an episode to watch. My friend said I'd like the Christmas episode, the one where the family is separated by a snowstorm. My mother calls in the middle of my Google search and I lose my train of thought.

This morning it's the pebbles of lint on my bed sheet. They stick to each other like Velcro when I pinch them between my fingers. I peel them off one by one into the trashcan, but they don't seem to want to take the plunge: The cotton strands hold on to each other in dramatic embrace. The lint balls clump together like snow.

Chinese brands of nuts and sunflower seeds sit on the kitchen counter. My father insists the snacks my mother brings home every time she visits are not even as good as the ones he can buy from 7-Eleven. He ends up eating my chips instead, forgetting to put the dip back in the fridge. Mold forms in thin lines around the crumbs.

My old drawings still hang in the den. The most recent one is of a frog, stenciled over plain gray paper. It lurks out from under a membrane of water, eyes delicately filled in.

She'll be visiting over break and asks if I need anything.

My teeth pick at my lips, trying to snag a layer of exposed skin. I peel the skin with my front teeth, coaxing the strip off, leaving blood beading. The wound stings every time I go out in the cold air. When a thin layer of skin grows to cover it, I run my tongue over the frayed patch and it opens like a zipper.

My friend waves at me in the halls, half-smiling from afar, saying something I can't understand. Most days I can't make him out in the crowds of people that melt by.

"All I Want for Christmas Is You" plays over the speakers as I get a filling. The drill keeps rhythm with Mariah's singing as spit fills up the cavity of my mouth and seeps down my chin. Stay still, please, or I'll have to start over again.

I still buy sketchbooks. The pages are thick and uneven, collecting graphite too quickly and smudging at the corners. Deep indentations layer the surface of the paper where I've pressed down too heavily. Some indentations go on for pages, causing the images on those pages to clump together. I peel them apart slowly, blowing on the graphite so it won't smear.

Early in the morning, citrus juice runs down my wrist, collecting at my elbow. Oranges take longer to peel—I dig down too deeply and some juice flicks onto my cheeks, watering my eyes. Later that day, an extra orange I brought for lunch crumples onto itself from the weight of my books. The juices slosh around the bottom of my backpack, staining my papers in tart, muddy watercolors.

On the way to pick up my mother from the airport, I peel at my cuticles without thinking. The streetlights pass by in thick, blurry lines as snow collects on the windows. I imagine her as an outline, her features becoming clearer until they're filled in, vivid enough to see.

A Muslim in Christendom

OMER HATIM, Grade 12, Age 18. Thomas Jefferson High School for Science and Technology, Alexandria, VA. Jennifer Seavey, *Educator*

"Snack time!" Like a swarm of ants rushing toward the last morsel of fruit on the sidewalk, our preschool class piled inside for snack. A banquet of graham crackers and apple juice was distributed around our table, with half the kids playing cracker dominoes, the others attempting to make the world's tallest Dixie cup tower. Ms. Reeves let out a high-pitched whistle, and all activities came to a momentary standstill as a line formed for pizza. I stayed in my chair. My friends came back with pepperoni pizza in hand, asking why I didn't take any. It was because I'm Muslim.

It wasn't really a big deal. I knew I had a peanut butter and jelly sandwich to eat instead, which I would argue is just as satisfying. But this was still one of a few nuances, among others, that set me out as the brown dot that didn't match with the rest of the portrait. The Vienna Baptist Church was the place where I met the first few friends I made when I came to America, got introduced to the beauty of a religion that I had no prior knowledge about, and was fortunate enough to play on the biggest preschool playground in Vienna. I wouldn't trade the experience for anything. But even if I was able to walk like my peers, talk like my peers, and laugh like them, I did not look like any of them or even eat like any of them for that matter. The four-year-old me wondered why I wasn't able to consume the same kinds of foods as my friends or why I never went back to the church on Sundays like they all did. I wondered why Santa didn't like me, or why we never had a Christmas tree like all my other friends did. I didn't understand what being Muslim or Christian was, or what that even meant. My parents never told me about my religion at the time. I later found out it was because of two planes that had crashed into the World Trade Center a month prior to my family's immigration.

My parents shielded me from what their religion had brought upon its followers. The heinous, vile atrocity that had resulted in the lives of those 2,996 being cut short had catalyzed an outpouring of hate against a religion that wasn't responsible for it. My parents quietly practiced their faith, refusing to instill it into their children for fear they would be subjected to the same sentiment they had been exposed to. I was essentially stripped of the luxury of adhering to a faith for more than ten years because of the actions of another group of people to whom I have no relation. I saw my parents praying and fasting, but I never knew why they even did it. I knew what my label was, and I knew that in the box of my elementary school student survey asking for faith, I was supposed to check "Muslim," but I didn't know much about what being Muslim meant. I just knew I couldn't eat pork.

But even if I didn't know what being Muslim was, I knew how it felt. It's the abrupt change in tone during a conversation when you tell someone your first name, Muhammad. It's the sensation of getting conditioned to the forty-four eyes in a class of twenty-two bearing down on you when the social studies teacher in elementary school mentions 9/11. It's witnessing your mother's decision to stop wearing the hijab after being ridiculed by a co-worker. The trade-off between embracing my culture and letting it go in order to appease the society I live in is not a decision that comes with ease. But why did this decision even pose a threat to my identity? How could I leave behind the religion from my homeland of Kashmir, a region whose very foundation is its identity, based upon its struggle as a Muslim state in a country where the religion is a minority? The lack of knowledge I had about my religion at the time fueled any sentiment I had regarding the disparity between me and my peers, but I could not be more wrong.

Almost ten years after my Vienna Baptist School days, as a fourteen-year-old traveling to my home country for the first time, a hodgepodge of thoughts were bouncing back and forth in my head while we went down Route 66 on our way to Reagan National Airport. How am I gonna talk to all my relatives? I barely know Kashmiri. What if they make me pray with them? Are they going to have food that doesn't incinerate my tongue? Anxiousness and a little excitement accompanied me as I tugged on my mom's refrigerator-sized suitcase and clenched my comparably minuscule carry-on bag in the other, walking into the terminal, trying with little success to keep up with my father's brisk pace. I kept an eye on my four-year-old brother grasping his ostentatious peacock backpack to make sure he wasn't too far back. We made our way past the other flight service lines that were stationed along the layout of the airport. Virgin Airlines, Korea Express, Etihad, Emirates. My empty-handed sister snagged a spot for us in line while the rest of us "bag handlers" trudged up to meet her. I pulled my phone out of my pocket and proceeded to engage myself in a game of

Candy Crush, when the navy-blue coat of a TSA officer caught my attention from the corner of my eye. I cannot forget what happened next. "Sir, you have been randomly selected for an additional security screening." My dad was taken away, from his family of five, for what seemed like hours. These eleven words directed toward my father made me wonder why they were even necessary. I felt the need to finally delve into what my religion was.

The vast amount of time I had on my hands during my stay in Kashmir was not spent idling around, watching goats making a mockery of themselves. I spent hours, days, weeks on end researching my faith, the tenets and values that it held, and what it stood for. My grandfather, who was a Hafiz, or an individual who has memorized and studied the Quran in its entirety, dispelled some of the principles I thought were heralded in Islam. I was exposed to a few of the verses for the first time: "Whoever slays an innocent unjustly, it is as if they have slayed mankind in its entirety, and whoever saves one it is as if they saved mankind in its entirety." I interacted with the townsfolk of the Kashmir Valley, people who beckoned me into their houses for food and tea, without even knowing my name. I learned about Islam from the people who embodied it on a day-to-day basis, and I learned I was not so different from my Christian brothers and sisters at Vienna Baptist after all. I learned that we shared the same reverence for Moses, Abraham, and Jesus, the same tenets of love and mercy, and the same belief in the law of reciprocity, that one mustn't do to others what they wouldn't do to themselves. My religion did not create a disparity between me and my peers. It brought us closer.

The nation that my family and I live in has approached the dawn of a new era, where a man who has vowed to ban children, men, and women—solely on the faith that they adhere to—is the new president-elect of the United States. The campaign rhetoric has served as the fuel source to a resurgence of ridicule and hate crimes against Muslims. Fear has run so deep within the throes of some Muslim communities across the country that the premise of immigrating—once again—seems more and more viable. But this need not be. The status of Muslims in a country so great will not be mended through an exodus. It is the small things, the day-to-day actions of kindness and humanity that will extinguish the fire. My mother bakes the same butter pecan cookies for her Hindu, Jewish, and agnostic friends that she does for her Muslim ones. My brother engineers skyscrapers made out of LEGOs with Alex and Melody, not just Ibrahim and Fatima.

The diverse Northern Virginia bubble I was fortunate enough to be brought up in will not serve me for the rest of my life. I hope to bring my experiences as a Muslim in Christendom out into my broader world for the betterment of all I meet.

CLAUDE STIKELEATHER, ***Ghost House 2: The Reckoning***, Grade 11, Age 16, Durham School of the Arts, Durham, NC. Carolyn Maynard, *Educator*

Code Literacy

PRIANSH SHAH, Grade 12, Age 16. Livingston High School, Livingston, NJ.
Jessica Rivchin, *Educator*

0700. Wake up to the soft chimes of my alarm.
0730. Eat. Pack my laptop, choose a watch.
0800. School. The world fades to black and white.
1500. After school. Should I invest time in robotics? Continue my research? Work on my startups? Every day, I stand in this endless arcade with a single token.
2000. Dinner. It's *roti-daal-bath-shaak*—a typical Indian dinner.
2250. I fall to dreamspace.
0700. Once again.

My life is a routine—the same repetitive, monotone existence every day. The only escape is expression; yet traditional forms of expression are inherently limited. Years of rules, additions, and revisions have imprisoned the unbridled creativity artisans of the past treasured.

Fortunately, there is an art form untouched by limitation—the modern tongues: C#, Python, Javascript. The time of the Romance languages is long gone; programming languages, more diverse and greater in quantity, have taken the reins.

My story is born of frustration and a fear of becoming stuck in the endless loop of life. In search of change, I found the Connected Challenge, an online hackathon. Hackathons center around a culture of creation but call for disruption—and it was precisely this disruption I needed in my life. My idea was simple: Put nearby places into a smartwatch. However, I didn't know enough about the platform to make a completed product; I submitted an untested design I thought was sure to be met with scorn.

Evidently, Pebble (a famous smartwatch startup) disagreed. They graciously awarded me with seven smartwatches to test on. Months later, at another hackathon, I finished my application. It wasn't terribly impressive—it identified nearby places, polled online for reviews/information, and allowed for connection to a nearby Arduino beacon to place orders. But it was mine, and I was proud of it. There's something to be said for the euphoria of accomplishment.

Although this had been a battle of confidence at the moment, it would give rise to a war of interruption as an addicting break to daily dullness.

Rather than remain in a fateful loop, I found salvation in abstract syntax. If the pen is the writer's sword, the computer is my lance. My fingers adopt a fascinating gait, striding across the keyboard, creating, deleting, painting a masterpiece with assortments of characters and colorful splendor. To dismiss programming as an unimaginative science is injustice. Code involves intricate efficiencies, graceful algorithms, and acute expressions of thought: It is a modern art.

As time passed, even robotics became tedious. The elegant disruption I sought gave way to a political, competitive atmosphere within my robotics team. I chose to leave and assemble a new group—one with democracy and tolerance in mind to erase competition. I collected athletes and designers, dancers and musicians; I founded Fawkes Robotics with the same principal goal of disruption I had sought out for so long. The bet paid off—we experienced dramatic success and revolutionized custom robotics; by erasing competition, I was able to encourage innovation and break away from tradition.

Disruption became my masterpiece, and code became my brush.

Shall I paint a neural network? With this brush, I can train a robot to identify color signals. The impatient observer sees basic color detection, while the tireless mind watches in awe as a machine gains sight. Or shall I interface a circuit with the keyboard? Mixing conductive playdough with a simple processor, I sculpt an interactive statue.

Are these on display at museums and in galleries? Not in the traditional sense—they were exhibited at World Maker Faire. There, thousands of makers gather and bring their beautiful creations to life for tens of thousands to appreciate—this is the mecca of modernity.

I cherish these fleeting moments, where a tinge of color disturbs the monotone projection of life. This is the true definition of a "maker"—an innovator who seeks out the creative beauty within disruption. I have embraced this identity—I have chosen, rather than been chosen, to undergo a metamorphosis. I have unchained the child inside me that seeks wonder and amusement, the spark of curiosity that yearns to be kindled into a flame. Distortion becomes disruption as I aim to achieve for the sake of satisfaction—to create for the sake of creativity. With the single-minded goal of innovation, I have finished my cycle; I choose not to labor, but to make.

The Invincibility Card

MEHREEN PASHA, Grade 11, Age 16. Choate-Rosemary Hall School, Wallingford, CT. Stephen Siperstein and Isabel Aguirre-Kelly, *Educators*

velvet frocks—the color of pomegranates—hang on gaunt shoulders like
crooked picture frames, loose threads fraying along with a brooklyn-laced
timbre. cheeks lightly rouged, black ringlets fanning over foreheads, salty
tears tangled in cupids bows and candied lips. her monopoly board lies
littered with paper money, plastic realty, and day-old cheerios—a
get-out-of-jail-free-card reality. all lemon drops, storybooks, & scented
candles. fingertips jammed in piggy banks and sofa cushions, vermillion
and rust like washed-up pennies. nosebleeds and bleeding sharpies on loose-
leaf paper. mothers telling darlings outside bathroom doors that "mommy
isn't going anywhere. she promises." two spoons of honey dipped in
lukewarm milk, a blanket of brilliant pinpricks like tiny constellations
embedded in a midnight ballad—bleak and all-consuming.

Farewell

TALIA GORDON, Grade 12, Age 16. Denver School of the Arts,
Denver, CO. Azar Kohzadi, *Educator*

in sitting by the windows,
sullen, having seen the sun
for the first time in days,
listening for the shrill chime
of child's forefinger against
thumb, snapping appreciation
into walls long accustomed
to the lilting song of poetry,
i am thinking about sound.
about the vibration of
vocal chord, about oddities
and wonders and the things
i have heard in calliope's
domain—reverb, rap, tap of
typing and scratch of pen,
leak of orchestral drama from
beneath the far door, and
in the spaces between silences,
the words i have come to
love, granted each time with
equal reluctance and quiet
pride and, by the windows,
wondering at what it is to
be the recipient of hearts,
of souls, of secrets, what it
is to be the unknowing

audience of a muse, also
unknowing of itself, both
the product of oblivion and
omniscience, having seen the
sun for the first time in days
and wondering at this
celebration of loss, we left
our voices in the drywall.
be quiet, do not wake them.
and now, in hearing for the
last time this particular
resonance, i am still sitting
in the sun and forgetting
the cadence of it.

Pulse (Stonewall, 1969)

ZOEY CARTER, Grade 12, Age 17. Douglas Anderson School of the Arts, Jacksonville, FL. Tiffany Melanson, *Educator*

I.

Bowie's voice cracks in and out, over and over
on a broken record as
jagged glass protrudes from the window frame
like the teeth of a shark, jutting from its enflamed gums,
the blood still dripping from its last kill.
Stagnant brown beer drips from the bar,
as in the streets
our bruised bodies retaliate,
beaten to stringy pulp and tendon,
broken ribs twisted inside our bodies,
so close to puncturing our lungs,
blinded and deafened
by the harpy cry of police sirens.
This will be our history:
batons swinging at our already limp bodies,
cries that pierce suffocating air and we
hope to God that it isn't our lover,
over and over—

II.

The heavy beat of club music
pulses through the floor
through humid, thick air, pierced
by the popping sound of gunshots.
I don't have time

to ask why
before I become a Lite Brite of bullet holes.
The draining carcass of a cow,
hanging upside down in a slaughterhouse.
And next to me
drinks left unattended, spilled, dripping down
into the still-gaping mouth of a man,
husband on top of him, arms intertwined
and twisted together like the gnarled branches of an old tree.
My mangled body laid next to them for hours.
All of us,
in rows, and on top of each other, in piles,
blood draining from our bodies
like the beat of the music
over and over—

Sugared

JULIET LUBWAMA, Grade 11, Age 16. Downingtown STEM Academy, Downingtown, PA. Christine Flickinger, *Educator*

i dance beside my momma
as she molds and moves the clump of cornmeal
white paste on brown hands
her hips capturing the sugar-speckled curve of sunlight
she once said
i was dusted in sugar
so sweet that people would try to lick it off—
that underneath,
i was a honeyed bourbon pie

i feel like air
pirouetting through the kitchen,
a cloud over painted hills
i say, momma, what do I look like?
and the twist of her lips and the gleam in her eyes say Angel
and i dream that i am one
till many years later
standing in a foreign home, a single grain of sugar in a spice cake mix,
a stranger in my own skin,
when i'm barely comparable
to an Angel

but right now,
momma grabs me by the hand
molding us together

like waxen clouds waltzing over clay-formed hills
cradling each other to craft ashes of earth
like white and brown sugar
like cornmeal and chapati
rolled into something delicious

Elegy for Summer Girl and Me

ANNIE CASTILLO, Grade 10, Age 15. George Mason High School,
Falls Church, VA. Carly Joy Miller and Karin Tooze, *Educators*

Lila's carried above my left eye at the temple
in a crescent moon scar slung low in the sky.
She ate cherries from a paper bag & spat fleshy pits
as far as she could & cursed for fun
where we sat in snaking branches of a live oak
overlooking a parking lot. I like nighttime more,
she said in between spitting & silence.
But she never finished the thought.
Earlier years: daisy chains & blonde hair & interlacing
fingers.
Our mothers' hands. Her laughter light as the dress she
wears.
This is how you can tell if a mirror's two-sided, her mother
says, & Lila's finger reaches out to mimic her.
Drawing away quickly, her eyes flash to mine.

I touch the scar. A colony of bees built a hive on that live oak
while Lila talked gender politics. Through paper-thin walls,
drones burst
into hot summer air. We stumbled. A dark gash bloomed on
my temple where a root jabbed. Lila's hands were slippery
with my blood and she paused. Your eyes look so blue against
all the red.
The words fell out. Lila, that's really fucked up, you know.
I think of overripe peaches we threw away as they browned &
oozed sticky juice

on their own skin. I reach up & feel the pale, rounded scar that lingers beneath my fingertips. Where my skull is most vulnerable. For a moment,
I imagine a cherry pit sits there instead.

Family of Four

JOYCE LU, Grade 12, Age 17. Hillsborough High School, Hillsborough, NJ.
Shawn Layton, *Educator*

I. Mom

Sunday morning:
I sit in the kitchen, hands snugly
Enveloping a mug of tea,
Listening to the sweet sounds
That drift from the living room.
My daughter is practicing
Mozart, or Haydn, or Vivaldi—
What's the difference, anyway?
Her bow pulls the strings,
The strings vibrate,
And what comes out is
The product of years of struggle,
Pushing her,
Driving her,
Shaping her
Into the girl in the living room.
How blissful it is to
Know that I have created
A human being
Disciplined enough to
Push and drive and shape
Herself.

II. Daughter

Sunday at dawn:
440 hertz screams bounce off
The living room walls,
Glancing blows,
Like when a break shot
Scatters the serenity
Of a perfect rack.
Sweaty fingers, raw at the tips,
Sweep up and down
The fingerboard.
Force equals mass times acceleration;
Therefore, if I dial up the force
I will accelerate
And accelerate
And there will be no braking,
No breaking point—
"No breakfast until scales are in tune!"
My screams aren't 440 hertz,
They aren't in the range of the human ear.
But I can feel them
Collecting,
Festering,
Somewhere between my temple
And my throat.

III. Grandmother

Sunday as the sun rises:
Are their stomachs full?
Two pots simmer on the stove.
There is a third bowl in the refrigerator,
Just in case.

My granddaughter is making her mother
Proud in the living room,
Practicing acrobatics of the hand
And of the ear.
She is a contortionist,
Twisting herself into whatever shape
Is demanded of her. Otherwise
She is a trapeze artist, swinging from bar to bar
Of the music with the dexterity and
Desperation
Of a cornered jungle cat.

IV. Dad
Sunday in bed:
My wife sits in the other room
With her hopes and dreams
Steaming in a teacup.
At what speed do wishes travel?
How much do they weigh?
At what point do they bring about
The breaking point of a girl
Who cannot bring herself to
Break away from the sawing that has been
Ingrained in her?
She inherited it from me, the
Need to work yourself raw
Until the scales are
In tune.

The Sanctification of an Eight-Year-Old

CAMILA SANMIGUEL, Grade 11, Age 16. John B. Alexander High School, Laredo, TX. Sylvia Vela, *Educator*

"Therefore you shall be perfect, just as your Father in heaven is perfect." (Matthew 5:48)

obsessive-compulsive. noun.
def. one. tangled wires, broken synapses; obsessions dusting the shelves of the mind,
delicate land mines causing tiny earthquakes at the skin's surface.
def. two. cyclical self-infliction of pain measured by way of an internal Richter scale
from daily migraines to fault lines like fissures on skin.

i am best characterized by seismic necrosis: internal turmoil and external self-detriment
tectonic plates of skin that fall away with every written and overwritten thought,
characterized by tics that only mean damnation for people like me; i etch
cracks in the dirt, uncover gleaming canyons, tiny rivers of blood. my fingertips are
torn open as if there were secrets, or maybe answers tucked between muscle sinews,
as if corroding each layer of skin will yield a new fingerprint, cleaner skin so i can start over;
the want for CLEAN is a timeline of resurfacing neurosis:
vices line up waiting in church pews

because to get to purification you have to tick them all off, but
they are each a mixed drink of desperation that tastes of
dirty coins and blood in your mouth
like something taking your life away—
i never speak about how i separated every
setting and image to keep the sad away from the happy.
before, it meant
watching school and its barrage of guilts wash down the
drain as though sins
were crawling under my skin, meant
remembering my legs touching the car seat weeks ago after a
bad day, and never touching that seat again. it meant
washing, washing, washing hands and wrists and arms every
ten minutes
until my baby oil third-grade skin shrank into itself like the
skin of a fruit in winter
and my arms turned into twigs
drenched by wet snow that only dried them further; freezing.
i fear someone will look at me and see the lapses of judgment,
like when i decided i was dirty and needed to be clean from
the inside
by feeding on guilt: quarter slices of bread, washed down
with frustration in bite-size stanzas.
i dropped to seventy-six pounds of wrong, wrong, empty,
clean, stop.

it makes people who speak of lining up pencils on a desk feel
like enemies.
CLEAN is the cut-up and raw inside of my mouth,
it is the gloved hands that the third-grade children gawked at
and the doctors in antiseptic offices winced to touch—
me, my child's soft extremities, washed and wrung until they

were no longer mine; they were
folded-up worry. mortification within paper continents of skin
fault lines of crayola scarlet rising to the surface: salt and earthquakes in the plate tectonics
of disorganized thought while i combatted diagnosis and prescription, and every night
the kitchen floor became a courtroom, the fruit bowl contents gavels;
soap and water, a sin.

the want for CLEAN took every thought and replaced it with images:
disjointed shards of eyes. mouths.

clean, perfect cannot be self-inflicted ladders of scars on the soft flesh
beneath an unparallel jawbone.
i know it cannot be smatterings of stretches, wet screams on my thighs.
and yet, i know perfect cannot be self-loathing and chronic disassociation
life spent cowering under a revolving door of vices
distractions and excuses melding together.

eventually i achieve redemption and righteousness without knowing i was rising:
not through my carnalities and failures
but through a comeuppance: spring outside a chapel
that no longer imprisons me with glistening promises of purity.
as it took me so long to learn,
perfect is,
many times,
unclean.

Of Bees and Brothers

JACLYN GRIMM, Grade 12, Age 17. Lake Highland Preparatory School, Orlando, FL. Jeff Schwartz, *Educator*

Metamorphosis

We were twins born three years apart,
more identical than not. He was born
in a hurricane, myself in a honeycomb.
He left slowly over months of decreasing
attention / affection / how does someone
find a word to describe running away backwards?
Later, I found a swarm of bees inside my throat,
crawling up to fill my cheeks with honey.
I pressed my lips against their hive,
told them: Don't worry; You are not alone.

Flight

I kept the drones in my hair and they crawled
in my ears and out my nose and eyes,
coated my lashes in yellow pollen with their minuscule legs.
When someone asked where he'd gone,
I opened my mouth and bees flew out.
They taught me the trick to flying (don't look down)
and how to forget people once and for all (sting them!).
They do not have family, they have:
an apiary / a colony / a hive / a swarm / a kingdom.
They do not run away, they fly home.

Sting

They fed me the food of the gods,
honey / ambrosia / nectar; got me drunk
and told me prophecies. They were buzzing oracles,
but even though they knew what was coming, they lied about it.
They flew around my head and told me what direction to walk.
People stayed away from us, an aposematic bee being
with a human heart and not much else. Am I their queen
or are they mine? They told me they loved me,
but my brother used to tell me bees can not be trusted.
When they stung me I told myself they could not help it.

Collapse

I found the first body when I brushed my teeth,
stuck between my back molars. The next morning
there were three caught in the back of my throat.
I asked my queen, How many ways can you say goodbye?
farewell / so long / Godspeed / adieu
When she died, I kept her body safe under my tongue
until I could speak again. When they were all gone,
I drowned myself in honey and wept for the bees.
We were diseased and destroyed ourselves and each other;
I was not sweet enough for them to stay.

JEREMY DONAHUE, ***Man Eater***, Grade 12, Age 17, Forest Hill High School, Jackson, MS. Renna Moore, *Educator*

Trolls

GAYATRI RAJAN, Grade 7, Age 12. Mason Middle School, Mason, OH.
Jillian Denman and Rachel Young, *Educators*

The news is a prayer we will never learn
how to murmur: the fluted hymns
of *The New York Times* or *Washington Post*,
mundane treacherous with tension.
When I read I always skip to the comments.
How much like lightning words can be,
soft, devastating, made for conflict but never
for calm. Our minds slide into war
like bones breaking—fresh and quick.
The recent hurricane or shooting quivers
in my chest. Every day, fresh news, fed
and then forgotten, a hum behind the chaos.
Sparring strangers, their instincts hostile.
We have painted ourselves clowns,
gory color absent of reason. That feeling
of closeness, an instant away from something
even more dangerous than you are—
a risk purer even than day

Shock Therapy

CHLOE KIM, Grade 12, Age18. Milton Academy, Milton, MA.
Chelsea Dean, *Educator*

"At the local high school, algebra was being taught on a blackboard. I couldn't decipher the equations: Laotian teenagers in this remote village were learning mathematics more advanced than I'd been taught at their age in America. Back home, I showed a photo of that blackboard to a mathematician. 'It analyzes the velocity of falling objects, like bombs,' he told me."
—Allman, T. D. "Laos Finds New Life After the Bombs."
National Geographic, August 2015

The moment they put a mask over my face
I remembered it all—the texture of crushed stone
and the smell of fire. Cherry pipe tobacco smoke.
Stepping stones locked in cuds of clay, footsteps away
from a bomb landed in '68. Hollow throats as dry
as inner cheeks of seashells. Everyone waits.
They get the wires in place and flick the switch
and suddenly I am the single streetlight in the village
of Phonsavan, flickering like a compass needle.
I am a baby crawling into a bomb crater. My country
died, so I moved to the moon. I smell the burning begin
and my limbs thrash into the dance my mother
danced when she caught up in flames, standing inside
a wooden house slouching into burning, time circulating
through time.

State of Emergency

DAQUON WILSON, Grade 12, Age 17. Richland One Middle College High School, Columbia, SC. Carla Brabham, *Educator*

It seems like we just keep repeating history
Why we keep doing the same stupid is a mystery
We're stuck in this vicious cycle of hate, violence, and people being dead
Don't you get tired of the pools and pools of blood shed

Trayvon Martin, Mike Brown, Philando Castile, Alton Sterling, Terence Crutcher;
all names of people wrongfully killed
And it's OK to be mad but riots and violence doesn't help to rebuild
It's OK to hurt, it's OK to feel the brutal sting of pain
But must I remind you that we must stay humane

Frederick Douglass didn't write for this
Harriet Tubman didn't lead us out for this
Martin Luther King didn't have a dream for this
And therefore we should not run away from this

Hundreds of years of slavery, hundreds of years of racism doesn't just go away
And we sit here, say one thing, and just go on about our day
What makes it worse is that a badge can protect you of being convicted of homicide
And when we demand justice we're mocked, spat on, thrown out, and flat out denied

We need a change and that only starts when we have a conversation
But breaking windows, starting fires, and causing more violence will subject our argument to invalidation
We keep doing things that allow our stereotypes to perpetuate
When we really need our voice to say something to educate

We can't let hate continue to divide us with his tyrannical wrath
We can't continue this horrifying, disastrous bloodbath
We can't forget our history because the problem will only grow worse
And we can't let skin color be the reason why someone ends up in a hearse

TONGUE4HIRE

ELISA ADY, Grade 12, Age 17. San Diego High School of International Studies, San Diego, CA. Natalee Whitlock, *Educator*

in english, the word for worship is church. in spanish, it is iglesia. one sounds like weeping unbroken by stormwater, the other like the burning of a lover's violence. on sunday, my mother works from eight to eleven. i do not see or speak to her. en domingo, my father drags me to church by the gold-bangled wrist. i listen to a sermon in a language still strange in my own milktoothed mouth. the man at the center of burning raises his hands. i map the suffering carved into his palm lines. perdonar y desterrar, he says, looking at me in the fifth pew back. i slouch in my seat to hide the shame on my face. my mother asks me to let go of her hand. i do not. she shakes me, rips the bangle from my wrist. i watch her stomp on the brakes and feel my seatbelt burn a diagonal line into my chest, cleaving me. i gasp, fish-mouthed in my above-water drowning. my ribs grow gnarled, split my stomach open, and dump the paint in me onto my mother's leather seats. she yells at me not to dirty her bmw. my father sits me at his soccer field. i look up into the sun to wet my lashes. don't do that, he says to me. it will hurt your eyes. i ask him to say it to me in spanish. he shakes his head no and walks away into the field, where a line of brown men spit and dance and laugh joyously. pinche cabrón, they call each other. i do not yet understand the heat of slang-syntax. i stare at the brown of my father's calves where mine are a bony pale. my half-sister sits to my left. all of my sisters lately are made of halves. i've only met one so far, but i know the rest are nothing like me. my mother will give me a half-brother in a few years, or so god tells me. i am also made of halves. in one language, i weep. in the other, i burn.

on sunday, my mother asks me home for dinner.
en domingo, my father invites me back to his soccer field.
no, i say.
it means the same in both languages.

Funeral for a Childhood Friend

ALEXANDRA KARAIM, Grade 12, Age 17. University High School, Tucson, AZ. David Sudak, *Educator*

I remember wide blue eyes caught
like fish in those bright reading lenses.
My father told me you would die. That was your
diagnosis. But I was so young, I was no doctor,
I was a believer in the make-believe and the hard-to-believe.
I believed in Heaven but not Hell, birth
but not death, the pulsing forwardness of time
but still the existence of timeless things, like being
tucked in at bedtime, like Mother, Father, Child,
like the wooden framework of my swing set
which had begun to pale like bones in the desert sun.
I believed in you, so real then, your legs
shaking as you passed each row of pews.
Each step was an offering.

I remember you
both nice and mean, like all kids are,
swinging a skinny fist at the tetherball as its
orbit plunged toward you. Did this feel like punishment?
A good Christian's guilt is her faithless friend.
Monday chapel, Tuesday chapel, Thursday mass,
Friday chapel, Eucharist Form B and prayer service
and breakfast after, Lessons and Carols, thumbing
through the book of hymns to find the processional.
I prayed for sweaty George to love me, for homework to
come easy,

for this and that and nothing.
Maybe you prayed for another heart, or maybe
you didn't pray at all.

Your mother and father have deep-red faces.
They're holding hands. None of us can eulogize you.
We take the usual shortcuts: Gone too soon.
A pleasure to have known. A fighter.
This is a strange reunion. We'll go our separate ways again.
We want to. I count the moments till I can forget again
those steps like offerings and your
pale freckled skin. Mother Claire
says the Blessing and we fall to our knees
to beg the world for meaning.

Bombs Away

HENRY HICKS, Grade 12, Age 17. University School of Nashville,
Nashville, TN. Freya Sachs, *Educator*

An ekphrastic poem inspired by *A South Vietnamese woman mourns over the body of her husband, found with 47 others in a mass grave near Hue, Vietnam, in April 1969* by Horst Faas

I imagine a day
where you feel the sun on your forehead
nice, comforting–
until your skin begins to crack
that evening. Though my experiences
with heat and yours may differ:
you may have enjoyed a hot day
until the sight of napalm
and tarry smoke, always present
on the closing in horizon,
came too often and changed your preferences
to cold. You long for death,
where your heart freezes and everything else
lacks something so hot as fire,
its scowl burned into your sight as your
family, your home lit up as a beacon
for helicopters to find the front.
America–Home of the Brave, what part
of this is courageous?
The protests across the sea are not
for you. They want their boys home. They want
to play ball, to go out and go see what there is to see

because only now do they realize how fleeting life is
and how present death can be, though they do not
have to face it. Everyone knows someone whose
blood has spilled
on your floor, but you wonder:
Who is left?
The woman who cut your hair last is dead.
The young child you lived next to is dead.
Your father's boss, who gave you treats when you were little,
is dead.
His daughter is dead.
Her ex-best friend is dead.
You see their faces on the backs of your eyelids,
and you've got scars tallying off everyone you've lost.
They're all accounted for.
You hold your eyes tight, only opening them
when you think you've built up enough tears
to cry, but, I am sorry, you have shed
far too many, the light is gone, and where your eyes
used to lie, there is only emptiness,
you are empty.
The sky is empty, this country is a
wasteland. It has been bulldozed. There is no light at the end
of the tunnel. There is darkness inside and on the horizon.
It is closing in.
The light in the sky is all that is left,
and it overwhelms you—you are not used to bright things
anymore. The sun is
blinding, but it's reflection
on the sand—
what the dust cradles—
your husband, the man who you learned

to love, the man who learned to love
you despite your faults, because we all
have them—this man is dead, and you
are dying. The chemicals in your lungs
will kill you, they said, and you wondered
how,
just how did they get there, you asked.
It's the boys come to protect you,
that are putting it there; and I am sorry
I am sorry I am sorry I am sorry I am sorry I am sorry I am
sorry that the short time you graced the Earth,
it seemed as though it was going to swallow you up,
it swallowed everyone up,
mass graves and military cemeteries
holding men,
women,
children,
armed,
unarmed, it doesn't matter—
they were scared.
We all die, but theirs were cut
short, and with so much death around—was everyone going to
die?
Was that the beginning? When will we put down our guns,
what will it take? Will we all be bloody,
gasping, and dazed?
God
must ask himself, what has he done.
Even the bugs and the buzzards
have more life than us.

Answers

JOLI BROWN, Grade 12, Age 17. Westover School, Middlebury, CT.
Thomas Juvan and Bruce Coffin, *Educators*

Even the bird, disappearing into its hole, knows that the
world goes on without it.
—Tony Hoagland

Even the badger, tracking the adder
in the underbrush, sees the struggle
of the anthill, how they scramble
at oncoming rain like a school of fish
startled by the plunge of a skipping stone.
Even the child, crouched on the beach, cradling sand,
feels the sifting through his fingers and knows
that not everything can be held on to. Yesterday
on my way back from the market, I saw a girl
pick at the ties of a carnival balloon secured to her arm,
concentrating only on a little red string. When she pulled,
it flew free of her fingers like dandelion seeds in the wind.
Even the balloon, knowing the tears of the child,
and the enormous weight of the world, rises.

Marilyn Monroe

ALEX CLIFFORD, Grade 9, Age 14. Charleston County School of the Arts, North Charleston, SC. Danielle DeTiberus, Francis Hammes, and Beth Webb Hart, *Educators*

She was origami—flesh like onion skin—
creases etched deep then deeper, bones
became paper, marrow like cellophane, folded
smaller, smaller until she hid from herself.
Creases deeper now, tighter, breathe,
she was claustrophobic buried beneath
bottles of Redisol, until she hid from herself.
Then dissolved like snow on hot asphalt.
She was claustrophobic, pressed between
celluloid and drawn with lipstick, until
she dissolved—snow—sinking farther and
farther into the filtered black and white photos.
She was shaped between fingers beautifully
sculpted until she was the consistency of smoke,
lighter than air, until she fell farther and farther until
her ghost of Nembutal and champagne lay
beautifully sculpted on the floor. Wilted like
wisteria on the hardwood, blonde hair fanned
around her head. Nembutal and champagne like a ghost
on her nightstand, illuminated by lamp light.
It's lighter there. Lying on the hardwood floor,
she became paper, marrow like cellophane
her skin illuminated by lamp light. Crumpled
beneath the weight of her own palms

She was origami.

Unsolicited Advice to a Gay Boy in the Back of a Classroom Who Can't Say No

AMIR KHADAR, Grade 12, Age 17. Fridley High School, Fridley, MN.
Cheryl Burghardt, *Educator*

After Tonya Ingram

When you find you have the devil inside you
and the other kids see it too
A boy with green eyes might ask you into the bathroom with him
Say no
The girls at school might try to hook you up with that one boy from chemisty
say no
Don't call them homophobic
As much as they are
Say I don't like the men who called me a faggot
and strut down the hallway.

When you finally come out of the closet
after a whole life hidden,
hiding from the heart inside your own body
Come out to everyone you know
Bust a hole in your childhood portraits
But don't get a hot or not

If your mother tries to beat Satan out of your body

Don't hit back,
remind yourself you still aren't broken
Don't find solace in staring at men who would rather see you dead than alive
Don't cry about the life you have,
plan how you will bust out of it

When you are walking down the hallway and the boy with the cute hair says
you have nice legs
You don't owe him any affectation,
you say thank you
boy with nice hair
and keep on walking
Do not take a second to question if your body belongs to you

When the strangers on the subway assault you with their eyes
and undress you with your skinny jeans,
Do not cross your legs
don't smile back
Don't put on your headphones and ignore them
Don't get off on the next stop
Bash their skulls with your eyes and strut off the bus

If the boy with the green eyes asks you into the bathroom
say no

When you go on tumblr and all the couples look ten shades paler than you,
ask why
But don't think you are not as high a quality as anyone else
Your skin is not a cancer

and it definitely isn't an open invitation

When you see a gay black boy shot in a gas station two miles away
because he looks like you,
cry
then remind yourself he isn't an animal
you aren't an animal
get your nails done
Untwist your queer body

When your mom bangs you against the wall,
Cry
and google what domestic abuse is
If you regret telling your mother your truth,
remember Satan could come from the most holy of holiest
and you are nothing but godly

When the boy with the green eyes asks to take you on a ride
say no

Just because you grew up queer you look at yourself funny
but that doesn't mean you aren't human
Your consent is as good as your humanity
That doesn't mean you can't say no
That doesn't mean you aren't worthy of saying maybe later
I don't want to
never
I don't like you

And if green-eyed boy doesn't listen,
grab the pots

grab the knives
scream his head off
kick his groin
Hold a gun to his head
Run down the street
Find solace in the SA bathroom

Do not find your fear as a taboo
Tell everyone he with the green eyes wants to take things
that are not his
Tell them he tried to rob you of your freedom

It is your body
you are precious
you are a diamond in the rough
nobody needs to unearth you after you did it yourself

You don't have to be a victim
But you will be a misunderstood ideology of strength
That hasn't yet been documented
Hold cities in your silence
I'd be damned if anyone looks at us like we're weak

Heirloom

MASFI KHAN, Grade 11, Age 16. Queens High School for Sciences at York, Jamaica, NY. Rachel Minkowsky, *Educator*

you are ten when a teacher says to untie
your bengali accent like an iron necklace.
you dream of having a voice that slices bones.
of being an autumn-crisp american,
even if it means silencing the pulse
you've carried since birth.

you unhinge slanted vowels, punctured
consonants, flitting cadence from your larynx.
lodge borrowed syllables in their places.
bangla slips out of your mouth like baby teeth.
you pronounce bleeding gums as maturity,
instead of your history withering into a speck.

your first month in america, your mother
kept warm by humming bangla songs.
her voice dripped with traditional superstitions,
pithas during monsoons. day by day, her ache
for the self left behind swelled like a ghost.

your last name traces its lineage to ancestors
ancient before colonization.
you can't yank your mother tongue
by the roots without erasing yourself.
in a country where nothing belongs to you,
bangla is an heirloom, sacred and tender.

let it seep into your journey
from dhaka to new york and beyond.

these days, you dream your mother still croons,
her homeland engraved on skin.
you cling to her lilt like air.

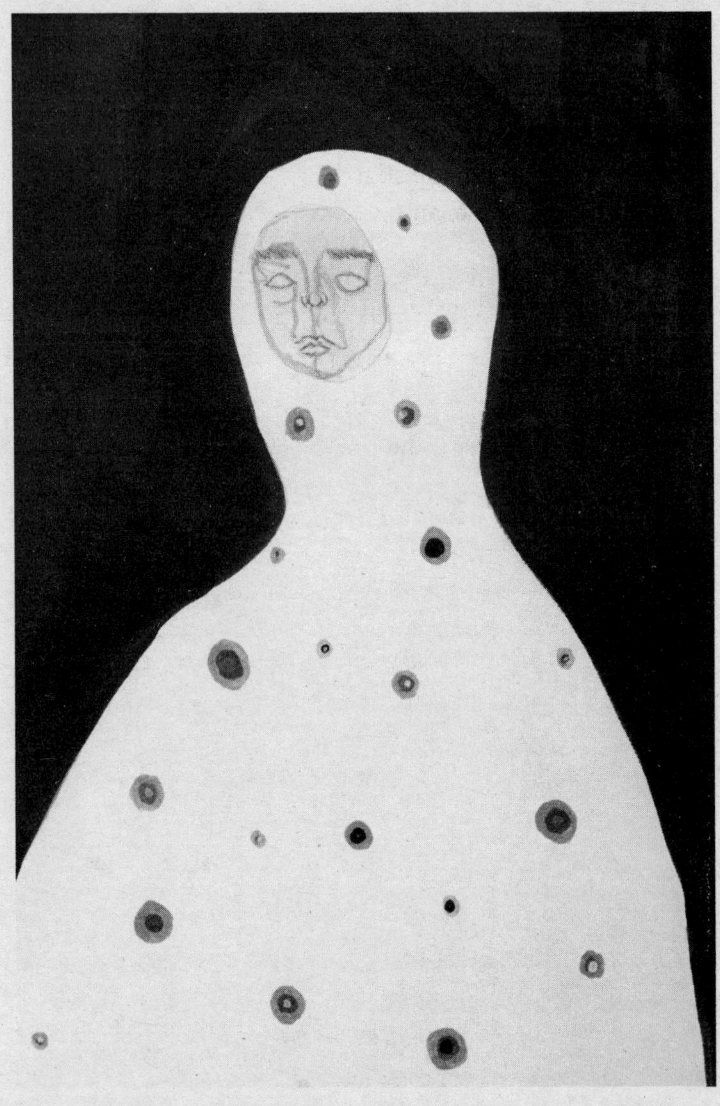

CHLOE MANVILLE, ***Empty Warmth***, Grade 12, Age 18, Bainbridge High School, Bainbridge Island, WA. Mary Rowland, *Educator*

April Showers

KALIAH WHITE, Grade 11, Age 16. George Washington Carver Center for Arts & Technology, Towson, MD. Rebecca Mlinek, *Educator*

Dark clouds were spread thickly across the Baltimore sky on a Friday evening. Every few seconds, the sound of thunder would resonate, accompanied by a spark of lightning slicing the sky. A chilling wind danced through the thick spring air and small droplets of rain began to sprinkle over the city. The storm had hardly begun, but people weren't willing to take the chance of getting caught in it. Many of them were in a rush to get home to their families, bustling to their cars and flagging down taxis. Inside the Paramount High School of Fine Arts at around 5:00, the school was empty of students and almost all the staff had gone home. Only three diligent staff members remained at work.

Mr. Baker was on the first floor of the school, cleaning the bathrooms. He liked to start at the top on the fourth floor and then make his way to the bottom. It had been that way for his past fifteen years working as the school janitor and he refused to have it any other way. As he scrubbed the toilets in the girls' bathroom, he began to think aloud. "Ought be a woman janitor in here," he said. "All this talk 'bout gender equity, or whatever they call it, and I still don't see nary one lady scrubbing no damn toilets. Not one in my fi'teen years I been working at this place." He scrubbed at an unidentifiable spot on the toilet seat with his rag and was satisfied when he made it disappear. "Least I don't gotta scrub the 'rafitti off the walls. No, no, no. Art schools don't like that type a stuff," he said chuckling to himself. He gave the linoleum floor one last sweep and made his way to the elevator. Mr. Baker hated the elevator but he didn't have a choice but to use it when he had to push his janitor's cart around, which was often. It was always difficult for him to fit his meaty belly and the cart through the door at the same time. After three minutes and many failed attempts, the old man had successfully gotten his cart and himself into the narrow elevator. He pressed the button to the fourth floor and tapped his foot with happiness to be done with the day's work. All he had to do was grab his keys from his office and lock up his cart on the fourth floor. As the elevator doors shut slowly, there was another loud clap of thunder, and the rain came pouring down a lot harder than it was before.

***

Tap . . . tap . . . taptaptap . . . taptaptaptap. Theresa Barnes, the secretary of PHSFA, sat behind her desk typing on her computer, messaging back and forth with Mr.Hunk79 on her new favorite dating site, DatesRUs.com. She'd been talking to Mr.Hunk79 (whose real name was Henry) for a couple of months online and meeting him at various locations, sometimes to talk and sometimes to do a lot more than that. Today he was supposed to come to the school. She switched windows on the computer so she could begin to log attendance. The office was empty and silent, which gave her the opportunity to get her work done, but suddenly, she heard a loud chime coming from her computer, letting her know she had another message from Henry.

MR.HUNK79: All right I'm almost there. Still don't see why I can't have ur #. Calling wud be easier.

THERESAFOX: Yeah, easier for husband to track. Just tell me when u get here.

Theresa spent the next ten minutes preparing to meet Henry. She brushed her soft curls, reapplied her lipstick, spritzed some perfume, and removed her wedding band. She reluctantly slid the delicate ring in her desk drawer and closed it shut. Moments later, when Henry arrived, she was all smiles. He walked in wet, carrying a briefcase and sporting black glasses with a thick frame. His button-down polo shirt was tucked neatly inside his chinos, and his loafers were soaking wet, as if he had stepped in a puddle on the way in. He signed the visitor's book and tried to talk subtly, barely moving his lips.

"Are you sure no one's going to be here?" he asked. He looked at Theresa seriously.

"Only the old janitor is here, and he just stays to himself. He's like sixty, he probably can't even hear very well."

"And the surveillance cameras?"

"We hardly ever look at them, but just in case, I told the principal you were my neighbor who was coming for a tour of the library. We'll be in the library's copy room, which doesn't have cameras. She thinks you're interested in working here."

"Doesn't sound believable."

Theresa sighed in annoyance. "Yeah well, she's gullible. Now let's go."

She led the way to the elevator and they walked in a businesslike manner. They made it just in time as the elevator doors were closing. "Hold the elevator," Theresa shouted, and Mr. Baker nearly got his pudgy hand crushed trying to hold the elevator for her.

"Mr. B," Theresa said once she was on the elevator, "you do know there's a button to open the elevator door, right?" She sounded condescending, he shrugged his shoulders and made room for Henry, scooting his cart out of the way.

"Who's this 'ere fellow, Theresa?"

"Oh, just my neighbor Henry. He's thinking about becoming a librarian here and wanted to get a feel of the library first."

Mr. Baker threw her a doubtful look. "Third floor then I s'pose?"

"Yup."

"Okeydoke." Mr. Baker pressed the number three and looked at the student artwork on the elevator walls as he attempted to avoid eye contact with Henry. He particularly liked one self-portrait of a woman looking into a mirror and seeing something much prettier in the mirror than what was there in reality.

Strawberry Swing

DARIAN O'NEIL, Grade 11, Age 17. Marlboro County High School, Bennettsville, SC. Sheila O'Neil-Brown, *Educator*

I nervously glanced up at the clock on the wall in front of me, probably fidgeting way more than I should have been. Each passing movement of its hands seemed to be purposely mocking me—ticks and tocks sounding off in rapid succession behind one another, but still taking an eternity to make a full rotation. With a small sigh, I slouched in my chair and buried my face in my hands. I was alone in this spacious lobby.

I had always hated hospitals ever since I was a small child. The overwhelming odor of antiseptic and iodoform was nauseating. There was an aura of helplessness that made me depressed. Worried pedestrians. Serious doctors. Robotic janitors. I once told her that if I ever became reduced to being propped up in a bed 24/7 with monitors beeping continuously behind me that she could just pull the plug. After all, I probably would be spending the rest of my life with this girl.

Ten years, I thought to myself.

That's how long I had known her. We had met when she was six and I was seven, and I'm pretty sure neither of knew exactly what love was at the time. I just knew she had a pretty face—

nothing more, nothing less. On paper, we definitely shouldn't have stuck by each other's sides for this long, but here we were.

A soft female voice interrupted my thought pattern. "Excuse me, sir, are you OK?"

***

Pushing nearly ninety miles per hour on the freeway fueled by pure adrenaline, I didn't really notice my surroundings. In my peripheral vision I could vaguely see the collective blur of cars and street signs I flew by, but I paid them little to no mind. I was sweating profusely in my thin sweater and jeans. I didn't know where exactly I was going, but I knew I had to get away. The thoughts started badgering at me again. Was this really what I had resorted to? Running away and abandoning all of my responsibilities? I'd be no better than my own father if I actually went through with this. Glancing into my rearview mirror, I noticed a startling parallel. I was starting to look more and more like him every day—or at least the man I had seen in the pictures my mother had shown me. Was that really who I had become?

I shook my head shamefully as I further chastised myself. Slowing down considerably, I took an exit and made a few turns, passing by all the major restaurant chains and gas stations along the way. Although I had barely been paying attention to where I was going, I soon found myself in a familiar area. A very familiar area.

I'm not exactly sure whether it had been some sort of muscle memory or an impulsive, deep-rooted desire to revisit the past, but I somehow had driven about ten minutes away from the neighborhood that we both used to live in. Ten minutes away from the park we had first crossed paths at—ten years ago. With a sudden jolt of levelheadedness, I knew right then

I couldn't run away. I had to be better than the man I'd never met who I sort of looked like. I loved her too much to just leave like that.

Now that I knew where I was, I certainly had some catching up to do.

***

The swing set was still there. It was leaning and worn out, but it was still there. It had been almost three years since I'd been here, and an instant rush of nostalgia washed over me as soon as I stepped out of my car. Dead, brown grass crunched under my feet as I approached the old park. Most of the playground equipment that I had enjoyed playing on as a kid still stood upright along with the swing set, including the monkey bars, seesaw, merry-go-round, and the slide. I felt a slight smile creep across my face as I reached the swings.

The last memory I had was the two of us meeting here one last time before I had moved away. "I love you," she had told me with tears streaming down her face.

I reiterated her statement with an "I love you too," and in that moment, we embraced. That was the first time I had felt love, and it would also be the last time. The next day, I had moved away. In a single instant, I recalled almost every memory we had shared together at this park. The laughs. The cries. The kisses.

Sanctuary on 811 Hansfeild Avenue

REBECCA AGYEI, Grade 12, Age 17. Metro Learning Center Magnet School, Bloomfield, CT. Thomas Macey and Emily Wright, *Educators*

Sometimes after school, I would ride my bike to 811 Hansfeild Avenue. Something about the abandoned factory and run-down gazebo engulfed in rose vines gave me comfort and provided me with safety from the dangers of middle and high school, boys, TV, and society's expectations.

I did a lot of thinking in that gazebo, most times I would think about how much I hated Mrs. Rigerou's class and everyone who laughed at me and my thick, jumbo butterfly braids. I never really understood why my hair suddenly got so much negative attention. My mom did the same butterfly braids for me all throughout elementary and middle school, and no one seemed to care or mind. Maybe it was after all the girls started getting relaxers and keratin hair treatments. I must've missed the memo, because I was the only one who still wore my nappy black hair in jumbo butterfly braids with hot-pink barrettes. I remember asking my mom to buy a relaxer kit for my hair. I desperately wanted to have straight, relaxed hair. I continuously harassed my mother to the point where she finally bought a relaxer kit for my hair. I felt a mixture of excitement and relief—I would no longer be known as Rose with the jumbo braids, I would soon be Rose with the long, straight hair.

My mother spent an hour and a half applying the relaxer on my painfully nappy hair; I was so anxious to see how it would come out and excited to rock my new soft, relaxed hair to school the next day. When my mom dried my hair and straightened it out with a hot comb and blow dryer, I realized that I had lost a huge chunk of my hair. The following three weeks were the worst three weeks of my middle school life. It looked like I had a total of four strands of hair; at least those four strands of hair were nice, soft, smooth, and straight. I went to school with a head scarf on for a month. I know for a fact that there was more snickering and whispering behind my back than there was when I went to school with my jumbo butterfly braids. Even my friends would tease me and call me "baldie." It didn't really bother me at first, but after a while I got irritated. Why did it matter so much if I didn't have nice long, soft, or silky hair?

I tried to ignore all the laughter and insults and told myself that I was not my hair, and that I was still beautiful. But for some reason, the sounds of laughter and mockery were louder than my own thoughts in my head. I tried to use makeup to get people to focus on my face instead of my hair, but because I had no idea how to apply mascara on my eyelashes the right way, not only were my eyelashes clumpy but there was also excessive ink on my eyelids. My hair was a source of laughter and now so was my face. I was living in a never-ending nightmare. I felt like all the *Seventeen* magazines, fashion advice columns, and makeup tutorials in the world couldn't help me get the look I wanted. School just became worse; I hated getting on and off the bus in the morning, just to walk into the gates of hell. Most of the time I was lonely, annoyed, and angry, but it didn't take long before I just became lonely and sad. I truly detested eighth grade. I wanted to go back to the time when the only thing kids cared about was snack time and how many toys or dolls you had to trade with.

When I transitioned from middle school to high school, the ridiculous expectations that I felt to look like a size 6 black Barbie with straight hair while being a size 14, nappy-haired fourteen-year-old only increased and made me feel unsure of myself. As I got older, I paid a lot more attention to the messages that certain programs and TV shows conveyed. The content was the same as it was when I watched it as an eight-year-old, but continuously being exposed to the same type of hair, same type of skin, and same type of body on the TV screen affected me more as a fourteen-year-old in high school. I would spend hours staring at models in *Seventeen* magazine and spend the rest of the day either starving myself to the point where my stomach developed a low-pitched growl or wasting the honey and organic fruits my parents would buy with their hard-earned money to make organic face masks in hopes that I would develop a "Hollywood glow."

The only escape from the torment was the comfort that the rose vines all over the gazebo at 811 Hansfeild Avenue gave me. I appreciated the exquisite yet simple beauty of the rose vines. There was nothing I could do or add to the rose vines to enhance their natural beauty. They were perfect the way they were and didn't need to be decorated with any glitter or paint to be even more beautiful. Yes, the rose vines had some nasty thorns and rusty leaves on them, but I accepted the imperfections. I think the imperfections of the rose vines made them even more beautiful.

The Swamp Monster of Bayou Genesis

KAYLA READO, Grade 11, Age 17. New Orleans Center for Creative Arts, New Orleans, LA. Anne Gisleson, *Educator*

***

I prayed to God and asked that the fruits of my labor
be spared the wrath of my name. Cause I knows
I may not be granted salvation but they do not
deserve to bear this existence without an eventual paradise.
—Jael Abraham, Unknown

Jael Abraham is my great-grandmother. Yes, laugh; I am well aware it's said she had no last name, no documents, no children. But tales do give kudos to her huntsman mentality; and just like a good huntsman, you learn to leave no tracks. You ask me her middle name? I'll tell you I don't know it. You laugh as if a nonbeliever. That's good. Cause it's what she'd want you to do: to laugh in disbelief, ridicule me for attempting claim on a folk tale, an urban legend. Yet the fog is dissipating, as it appears to me those of you here are trying to dirty the soil of my foremothers. And as it has been for generations, her identity has been purposely shrouded in mystery. Many of my family have gone to great lengths to protect Jael, as she is the fleshly manifestation of what you would call a familial crest. Yet I am here, in indignation to provide you men with the following account: with hope to dissuade this government's wrongful denial of both my people's land and Jael's name. A name you have unapologetically smeared. So sirs, if you will, the time seems to be ripe for storytelling. And like all good stories, we are starting from your beginning, with appropriate modifications of course:

And as they say . . .

The first swamp monster was a woman.

***

My daddy had been good to me. But there was talk the black devil

danced inside him. Talk of me being a devil child.

If not the devil child

me and him shared kindred spirits.

Bastards baptized brutalized and bitter.

—Jael Abraham, Unknown

Jael. No last name. Daughter of slaves. Mother was Apphia. Father was Zacharias. Jael had a couple of brothers and sisters. Naturally, as Apphia is "fruitful" in God's word. Apphia and Zacharias were charming slaves. Apphia was a brown woman, honey-colored—while her husband had skin like molasses, real dark and ebony. Apphia was a woman of kind disposition: Her laugh was fluffy like fresh cotton, bouncy, her skin was a pastel cinnamon shade, sunlight would hit her to create a saturated brown haze on her flesh. The kids' complexions were mixtures of the two, but no matter the dissimilarity, each child had their father's doe eyes and their mother's button nose except for Jael, who had the eyes of a coyote, and the nose of a baby deer. Apphia was said to have been cursed by the birth of Jael—a birth in the middle of a river, all alone. There were rules to abide, circumstances evoking caution, circumstances around nature. Especially weather.

Jael was conceived in the midst of a hurricane—lightning cracked the blanket of fleecy clouds in lavender ultraviolet luminescence. The sinister wind hissed. The trees softened with patience. Hurricanes were signs of God's wrath, his utter disapproval of humankind's sinning. Many assumed it a warning from God that he wasn't afraid to pull an old trick out of his beard. Hurricanes were God's rage breathing wet heat through the area. But it was said too, that Lucifer would sneak up out of the dirt, in a pressed suit, wandering for lost people. When God was busy with fogging or soaking up everyone, Satan would saunter in all slick, calling lost souls to him. Said he would possess men, use their body, share their consciousness, and sleep with their women.

And as "God remembers," Zacharias was a suitable name for her father. Zacharias was what dark-skinned men are called now: dark chocolate. He was a slave so attractive the slave masters wished to mate him with the prettiest: lightest of the field and house slaves to see the outcome. One almost went far enough to encourage his daughter to investigate his flesh, absorb his seed, to see the product. Zacharias was a man of God, a somewhat preacher. Somewhat, because it was treason to the plantation for the slaves to gather in large numbers. But he spoke the word anyway. Zacharias's body was tall with very little muscle; he was not buff, which made the grueling field work of the men a hefty responsibility.

Yet with his poor luck, he was out hunting when a fog

closed off all paths around him. Zacharias returned home in bedraggled dress, seizing Apphia by the wrist, roughly dragging her about in circles as a form of dance. She, already arrested with Zacharias's broad torso, slender waist, and dark skin, had seemingly been twirled out of her garments, giving herself up on the floor. They wrestled with a feverish agony until early morning, Apphia's breast sore as she carefully pulled her clothes back on: Zacharias disappeared during her slumber, returning later with vacant eyes and a hollow chest.

The Sand's Silence

SAIRA BHATTI, Grade 11, Age 16. Parkland High School, Allentown, PA.
Candace Brobst, *Educator*

I imagine lying down on the sand and pulling the foamy waves over and around me, like a blanket. The water would recede gradually from the coast, taking parts of me with it. There's my freckles, my dark hair, the surface of my bronzed skin, all mixed and bobbing up and down in the inky harbor. And there are the letters too, swaddled up in creamy envelopes with exotic names written on them in my father's shaky hand. I suppose they are a part of me now as well.

I remember feeling the cool white sea spray from the open window on my eyelids that morning, the faraway sound of the waves rushing in and away from the coast, not unlike the secretive whispers of two parents. I blinked the sleep out of my eyelashes, the cracked, pale-pink ceiling of my bedroom coming into focus. My eyes wandered to a peppering of roses that I painted on one corner in an artsy teenage phase and fixated there, a fistful of mellow thoughts warming dimly in the back of my head. It was quiet, so quiet. I could've been in that house by myself all along. But he had never left me before, not this early. I swung my legs off the bed and felt the floor purr beneath me as a roll of thunder shook our rickety house, the nicks in the cool hardwood palpable under my threadbare-stockinged feet. I wandered out of my room and into the foyer, brushing my fingertips into every chip and crevice of the loved, pastel paint. The crude curvatures of my rogue childhood cave drawings were shadowed underneath patchy coverups that were the wrong color. I smiled. My father sat at our table, facedown on his woven, spring-green placemat, fast asleep despite the sun softy climbing up in the sky. It looked like a candle that was about to be blown out, as the sad, heavy clouds would wrap their intoxicating grayness around it soon. I heard a seagull caw somewhere outside. It was so quiet.

***

It was delivery day, and an indigo storm smiled darkly on the horizon like a gray-gloved mortician. It was never supposed to thunder on a delivery day. I shook my father awake, the rough-hewn wool of his sweater pricking my fingers.

"Pa," I murmured, my fingers barely grazing his limp form. "You can't go outside today. It's going to rain, and I'm sure even the youngest, bravest fisherman in town is staying warm and safe at home."

The word "safe" caused his eyes to snap open. I suppose that's the exact word a father wants to hear, safe, safe, safe. He sat up slowly, and the ancient bed frame creaked tiredly. There were seventy-five years of shipwrecks in my father's eyes. His gaze traveled to me with a syrupy languor, all the while shaking his head.

"Nobody can be glorious while they're warm and safe at home, my girl." I slid his kitschy teacup away from him, the porcelain chilly and the tea cold. "Nobody can be glorious while barely making enough money to survive and spending half of it on pretty stationery to drop into the ocean." He flinched sharply away from me, as if I had struck him with the heat of my breath. I looked down at my hand and was surprised to see that there was nothing there, as I felt I had torn the color from his cheeks and ought to be holding it.

"I'll deliver the letters," I blurt, too loudly, brandishing the single empty envelope like a sword, "I'm not helping you by sitting around here anyway."

My father's face darkened and he laughed his dusty laugh, salt-and-pepper beard quivering.

"You're afraid of the water, my dear." He was right. I was.

At noon, I packed my father a lunch in the dented tin lunchbox that I got for my sixth birthday, the last birthday gift I had ever received. I gave him two thick slices of stale bread and a thimble of peach jam, a fistful of napkins on the bottom giving the meager supper the illusion of bounty. As an afterthought, I scrawled a note on the topmost napkin with a runaway stick of charcoal and shut the flower-embossed lid, which didn't quite fit right. I don't even remember what the note said. If I had known that those words would be his final memory of me, I might've thought of something profound. I'm glad I didn't. I'm not profound, and it's a bitter thing for a lie to be the last snake out of your mouth and into the ear of the person you love most in the world. I bent down to hug him as he left, wearing that red, cable-knit cardigan that was older than I, a fisherman's chain mail, realizing how small he really was as he wandered farther and farther away. Dropping letters in the ocean, indeed. The sand was gray with storm.

I spent the next few hours busying myself about our crumbling gingerbread house, colors in my eyes and sharp objects in my hands doing great things to fill my mind with beautiful nonsense. Straightening fading picture frames that I had never noticed were crooked. Rifling through my few possessions—a shiny, enamel-painted spoon I had once found on the shore, an assortment of candy-colored seashells and seaglass that made music in my hands, a wilting pink carnation that a boy had once given me a long time ago. The flower crumbled in my hand. A blue cameo pendant on a thick, tarnishing chain that I liked to imagine was my mother's, but I never knew my mother and reckoned that she didn't know me either. A pair of worn satin ballet slippers in a dirty lilac color that I had found in a cabinet one day, giving me dimly lit childhood dreams of one day becoming a dancer. A child with ambitions always grows to be an adult with regrets. I shut the slippers back into my drawer and abandoned my rose-wallpapered cage for the parlor, its peeling green paint and dark wooden panels looking empty without my father in their palm. Muffled thunder roared over the canned sound of the television, the people's vivid, smiling faces too bright and colorful for my unstable world. After a long while of listening to the white noise, I shut every light off and resolved to go out and find my father. I pictured him having one of his forgetful spells while the waves tossed him from crest to crest, a child's plaything, and my blood was shot through with cold anxiety. It had never rained before on a delivery day, not in all my years. I saw his murky eyes running electric green with panic, saw his crooked, stocky form tossed into the tempest without mercy. I was tingling to the bone, my heart banging against my ribs, a clipped bird flailing in a crumbling cage. I needed to leave. I was leaving.

The China Bird

ESTELLA ZHOU, Grade 7, Age 12. Prospect Sierra Middle School, El Cerrito, CA. Mara Hornillos, *Educator*

"Down with four-olds!" Zhang He said suddenly. "Down with four-olds! Down with four-olds! If we're going to be Red Guards, we have to know how to chant! Come on, do it with me!" Rong Lin joined enthusiastically, and the other two began to clap their hands in rhythm. Soon their voices grew louder and louder, until finally Ming Gao and Rong Lin fell out of breath.

"Come on," urged Zhang He. "You can't just stop when you're tired! That's just plain bourgeois! At least it's what my brother said." She shook her head, as if disappointed in her friends. Ming Gao took a breath and obediently began to chant again, this time louder, with forced momentum.

"Just because your brother is a Red Guard doesn't mean that you're in charge of us!" Rong Lin protested.

"If you even hope to be a Red Guard one day, you'll have to be stronger than that," Zhang He declared importantly. Rong Lin shrugged. But she continued to chant with her friends, not stopping until they had reached the schoolyard.

"Over here, Zhang He!" cried a boy who stood with a cluster

of other students. He smiled, revealing a mess of crooked, yellow teeth. No wonder we call him Crooked Teeth, Rong Lin thought.

Crooked Teeth beckoned Zhang He over. “Our brothers are both Red Guards!” he said excitedly.

Zhang He and Rong Lin ran off to join the group. Ming Gao followed, her black braids swinging around her chubby face.

“Go on,” urged Ming Gao. “Tell us more!” She clung on to his arm and pleaded.

Crooked Teeth shook her off and ignored her.

“We need to help our country, comrades. Today, we will all be Junior Red Guards. Zhang He and I will lead. Who’s with us?”

For a second, everyone was silent, as if thinking this over. Then suddenly everyone was shouting, “I’ll join! I’ll join!”

“Quiet!” shouted Zhang He. “Ming Gao, you’re treasurer. You have to write down everyone’s names.” Ming Gao obediently took out a pen and paper from her backpack and scribbled everyone’s name. At last, she came to Rong Lin.

“Are you joining?” Ming Gao demanded. Rong Lin didn’t know what to say.

“I’ll join,” Rong Lin mumbled. She didn’t know who her friends were anymore. She had helped Zhang He and Ming Gao with their homework ever since they were together in first grade, explaining math problems until they understood everything. Why was Zhang He suddenly so different? Was it because of all the Red Guard business?

***

“Come on, Rong Lin,” called one of her classmates from the crowd. “This way! Today we’re going to burn books at Imperial Booksellers and Rong’s Books!” Rong Lin froze. Students rushed past her, some on bicycles and others sprinting. Her classmates were going to burn books at Rong's Books? That was Grandmother's shop!

Rong Lin fought her way through the crowd to the group of Junior Red Guards. She wanted to say something, but in panic she couldn't. Instead she followed her classmates away from the school and toward the city center.

In the middle of the street in front of Imperial Booksellers, a bonfire blazed. Red Guards were running from the bookshop with armfuls of books and tossing them into the fire. Rong Lin watched in horror as the flames swallowed the books, devouring the pages and blackening the spines. A crowd of people had gathered around the scene, watching the Red Guards burn books. Her classmates ran into the shop. A moment later, Ming Gao and another girl carried out a small bookshelf, and together they heaved it into the fire. The rest of the Junior Red Guards cheered. As the crowd shoved forward to see the shelf burn, Rong Lin slipped away. No one saw her leave.

She ran as fast as she could down the streets, her feet landing on the hard asphalt again and again. She had to warn Grandmother!

A crowd had gathered in Grandmother's street as well, and Red Guards were milling about the bookshop. A frail old lady stood by the door, barring the way from the Red Guards. She was shouting something, but her voice was swallowed by the crackling flames and the shouting crowd. Rong Lin realized with horror that the frail old lady was Grandmother. She pushed through the crowd and ran to Grandmother's side.

"Grandmother!" she cried frantically. Grandmother pushed her away.

"Go, run away," she hissed. "Stay away from here and don't come back until the Red Guards are gone!" Tears began rolling down Rong Lin's cheeks.

"I can't go!" she cried. "You need help!"

"What can you do now?" Grandmother asked. Just then two Red Guards seized Grandmother's shoulders. They pulled her from the shop, and more Red Guards rushed inside.

"Grandmother!" Rong Lin cried. She held on to Grandmother's hand as tight as she could. But another Red Guard hit her hand away and Rong Lin recoiled in pain. When she looked up again, Grandmother had disappeared, and the truck parked by the shop was pulling away.

"Grandmother!" she cried again. Rong Lin pushed herself to her feet and began to run again, darting past Red Guards and after the truck. She ran until she could run no more, and dropped to her knees on the ground. Tears streamed down her cheeks, a river of sadness. They had caught the little bird with white feathers tinted with pink that was Grandmother, and had muffled its songs and cries. The little bird would never sing freely again. Suddenly, Rong Lin's despair turned to anger. She began running again, ignoring the pain in her chest and the ache in her feet.

That evening, Rong Lin lifted the white stone in the yard and began to dig. Finally, a small patch of white appeared, smooth and cool, then some pink. She pried the little china bird from the soil and held it tight in her hand until it was warm. Then slowly and carefully, she set it onto one of the branches of the trees in the yard, where all could see it, and it could see all. There, it could sing freely. Nothing would muffle its cries. As she turned to go, the last ray of dusk light fell onto the tree, setting the little china bird's eyes aglow. No one could silence it now.

The Oracle

BEN CONNOR, Grade 11, Age 17. Mt. Pleasant High School, Wilmington, DE. Michele Weiner, *Educator*

Lycurgus's mind wandered as he waited, back to the day he had begun to worry. It had been a sweet summer day and supper was a spread of honey cakes and fish. Lycurgus and his wife, Megara, had sat down to dinner with Lycurgus's father, and all had eaten in peace. Then the pains had begun. A deep, gouging stomachache plagued Lycurgus immediately after his supper. He could barely stand, could barely move, and screamed through the night as his father and wife knelt by his side in fear. The pain passed, and Lycurgus might have dismissed it as a bad meal if not for what had happened in early autumn. As the air began to chill and the leaves began to fall, another attack had come. After dinner, Lycurgus had simply collapsed, agonized. This time the screams had lasted well into the day. And so it went, into a miserable winter and a dismal spring: occasional nights of wrenching pain drove Lycurgus to the extremes of agony. It was a terrifying lottery, not knowing when the next spell would strike.

Then came the real terror. His wife, Megara, had gone to her parents' farm, many miles from Athens, to visit them. Kratos, his father, had traveled to Corinth for business. Lycurgus had been blessed with a week of solitude. And the pains had stopped. It was the first time he had gone a week without an attack in many months. When Megara and his father had returned, the pains had begun anew. Lycurgus had drawn the logical conclusion.

So here he stood outside the grand temple, placing himself at the mercy of the god Apollo. Lycurgus could no longer live with this pain, and so he had come to ask the Oracle for answers. Could the pain be stopped? What—or who—was causing it?

"Enter," a stony-faced attendant at the doorway to the temple beckoned. Lycurgus scaled the stairs nimbly, and both men walked into the long hall that led to the Oracle's chamber.

They plodded down the antechamber slowly. Lycurgus's eyes were fixed on the bright bronze doorway ahead, flanked with golden eagles. When they reached the end of the hallway, the attendant stopped.

"The Oracle of Delphi," he said solemnly. He opened the door and stepped away.

Lycurgus was struck first by the stifling smoke that filled the room. It was a dry smoke, one that seemed to crackle as it floated toward the ceiling. Small green lanterns on the walls of the chamber gave the room its only light, which flickered sporadically in the haze. Lycurgus moved warily through the fog, half-afraid of walking straight into the Oracle, an act which he supposed would lessen his chances of receiving good advice. He could feel the uneven cobblestones beneath his feet and could smell the strong odor of burning incense. The room was silent.

All at once there was change. As Lycurgus walked further forward, the smoke began to clear, the odor grew stronger, the cobblestones gave way to solid marble floor, and Lycurgus beheld the priestess of Delphi. She was frightening in her simplicity, seated on a three-legged stool before him. She was dressed in a short white skirt and purple hood, the cowl almost covering her placid countenance. There was no chair for Lycurgus, so he stood patiently. The silence was deafening.

Slowly, the priestess nodded at him. Lycurgus cleared his throat.

"O wise Oracle, I am troubled by suspicion. I am afraid that one of my closest kin, my wife or my father, is plotting to kill me. I come to you for answers, wise Oracle. I come for sooth and assurance." He paused, feeling the weight of a month's dread fall off of his shoulders.

The priestess lowered her eyes, and the hood covered the entirety of her face. In wispy bursts, smoke began rising from a small hole in the floor. It had not the pure quality of the smoke surrounding the door, but a darker, more sinister spiraling quality to it. The priestess bent down and breathed in deeply of the sullied air, and Lycurgus coughed as the choking fumes began to surround him. The Oracle straightened up suddenly, throwing back her hood and revealing her pale and terrifying face; only the whites of her eyes were visible. She suddenly began to shake. Her hands beat at her legs slowly at first, then, in a frenzied crescendo of agitation, faster and faster until the Oracle's entire body vibrated. The smoke was now pouring out of the ground. The priestess opened her mouth and, in a raspy voice that sent chills down Lycurgus's spine, intoned, "Listen well, O Athenian, to the words of Apollo."

Lycurgus nodded vigorously.

"You search for the truth in vain. You will die—soon—at the hands of one whom you trust." The Oracle breathed furiously. As suddenly as the prophetess had straightened up, she bent down again, her hood concealing her eerie features. The rising current of smoke abated. There was silence in the room as Lycurgus stood in shock. He swayed slightly in a dreamlike state, heightened by the slight wisps of smoke that still clung to the chamber's dense air. He spun around and ran out of the chamber, his sandals slapping noisily on the stones.

Lycurgus dashed down the long hallway and burst out of the temple hurriedly, his breathing heavy. The sun that had warmed him that morning now beat down on him like a hammer, and he had a splitting headache. He couldn't breathe. Possibly the fumes. Lycurgus was hyperventilating, and he stopped not far from the temple to sit on a flat rock and catch his breath.

So he had been right. One of his own family was betraying him, though the Oracle hadn't seen fit to say which one it was. Lycurgus thought of his father—a man he idolized, a man of good repute in Athens and Corinth, a titan of industry and a kind father. Lycurgus could not, would not imagine his father trying to kill him. His thoughts turned, inexorably, to his wife. The sweet maiden he had fallen in love with in his school days had become his confidante, supporter, and friend. They lived together in what Lycurgus considered pure bliss. Kindred spirits. Tears came to Lycurgus's eyes.

Perhaps it could be someone else. What had the Oracle said? "One whom you trust"? Lycurgus thought for a moment. There were others he trusted. There must be. There were childhood friends, relatives, neighbors, many people. But did he trust them? He respected them, to be sure. But he had that kind of bond, that essential trust, with no one but his closest kin. And so there were two. His father or his wife? His wife or his father? His trusted companion or his mentor and idol? Which could do this? Who would try to take his life?

Lycurgus heaved himself up off the rock and began the long journey home.

Dinner that night was like a nightmare. Lycurgus ate in a dreamlike stupor. He sat across from Megara, watching her face with a terrified fascination. This was the face of his wife. Or the woman who was killing him. Which? His father sat next to him, chewing placidly and talking of his next voyage. Lycurgus did not look at him once. The evening was torture. Megara wove and Kratos mended a table, the two chatting optimistically all the while about Lycurgus's stomachaches and how they might be prevented. It drove Lycurgus to the depths of human anguish to know that one of the people before him was lying about their hope for his well-being. But why? What cause had he given anyone for wishing death upon him?

A Collection of Current Event Satires

JOHNATHAN STIMPSON, Grade 12, Age 17. Darien High School, Darien, CT. Sybil O'Hare, *Educator*

Inaugural Issue: The Daily News Weekly

Lobbyist Now a Regular at Senator's Office

After visiting the office of Arkansas Senator Tom Cotton (R-AR) six times last month and leaving sizable donations in the undisclosable, dark-money, super PAC, and . . . 100 percent legal tip jar, ExxonMobil lobbyist John Richards has been upgraded from occasional customer who stops by when convenient to a reliable regular.

Every lunch break, Richards can be counted on to order a hefty serving of fiscally irresponsible tax cuts, with a side of reduced labor requirements. "You got it," Cotton replies, scribbling down his order on a yellow ticket to hand off to the chef. "Anything else we can do for you?" Cotton cheerfully adds, before asking if he would like napkins with that. "We make a mean comprehensive, multibillion-dollar subsidy program too, you know." While Richards usually demurs, he always promises to try it next time.

"He's one of my best customers," Cotton admitted. "I don't even need to ask for his order anymore." As Richards said, "It's gotten to the point where I walk in and the industry-wide tax cuts and financially reckless corporate handouts are already waiting for me in a brown paper bag."

Crack Addiction Changes Middle-Aged Father for the Better

Susan Wallace, wife of 56-year-old accountant David Wallace of Connecticut, was surprised to learn last week that her husband had been abusing a form of powdered cocaine, a highly addictive substance banned in every state except Florida. Mr. Wallace, who was often described by family friends as a "dull log, slightly more awake than a comatose patient," never liked taking risks or acting spontaneously. Before his addiction, "he shopped from the eight-dollar bin at Kohl's, drove a Nissan Altima, insisted on eating at Olive Garden, and got his hair done at Supercuts," said Susan, struggling to hold back tears. Only just a couple of weeks ago, "he would come home from work and drool as he listlessly watched Fox News," David's sister-in-law Barbara added, noting just how much his addiction had changed him.

"Now, he's an entirely different person," Susan said. "Crack has changed my husband from an apathetic accountant to a fun-loving, energetic, if occasionally delusional, father." While the jitters and occasional shivering were annoying at first, according to Barbara, "I'll take addicted, erratic David over that indifferent lump of tissue any day."

At press time, David was planning to purchase a motorcycle in order to jump the Housatonic River in midair. When asked about his devilish antics, Susan grinned and said, "It feels like I finally have my husband back."

Meet Donald Trump

Political Ideology: Currently nativist conservative. We'll let you know when that changes.

Will He Be Elected?: Yes, after electing the first black president, it would be unreasonable to expect America to do the right thing twice in a row.

What Was He Like in Middle School?: Used to steal Jeb Bush's lunch money.

Biggest Achievement: Turned Dad's ten billion into eight billion.

Greatest Political Strength: Impressionability of the average American voter.

Reason for Running: Check off last box on bucket list.

Odds All of This Began Because of a Lost Bet: Far too high.

Favorite Method for Selecting Deeply Held Political Beliefs: Dartboard, coin flip, *Wheel of Fortune* wheel.

Reading Level: He says he's more of a math guy.

Initial Vision for Campaign: Raise value of Trump brand, free television time, bolster corporate holdings.

New Vision for Campaign: World domination.

Are We Just Enabling Him?: Yes.

"Christmas Will Not Be Coming This Year," Trump Declares, "Santa Claus Has Been Deported"

SAM CLARK, Grade 9, Age 14. South Pasadena High School, South Pasadena, CA. Diane Shires, *Educator*

With various protests to Santa on the rise, ideas for an alternative gift-giving process have emerged from every corner. President-elect Trump presumed that the toys would not be missed, but when pestered for an answer, he delivered.

"Well, it seems we'll just have to have Mexico pay for it," Trump claims. "I mean, they're already paying for my ingenious two thousand-mile border wall, so it wouldn't be hard for them to go the extra mile and buy presents for every single American citizen! I'm sure they'll be happy to comply, and if not, I'm ready to have Vladimir Putin talk some sense into them, if you know what I mean."

As appealing as holding Mexico for ransom sounds to die-hard Trump supporters, the rest of the country is looking for a sane solution. Vermont Senator Bernie Sanders aims to appeal to the opposite spectrum of die-hard fans.

"If Trump bans Santa from the USA, America must take action!" Sanders bellowed at a rally. "With effort and determination, we can raise enough revenue to purchase all the wishes for all of the children in America! The only slight catch is that to raise the necessary 600 billion dollars in ten days would require a temporary, week-long, 1,200 percent tax increase."

Although it is pleasing that the Jewish Bernie Sanders cares more about the integrity of Christmas than the Christian Donald Trump, such a tax increase is unheard of. No matter the case, the tax would be pointless, because every American would be spending the money it takes to purchase a present in taxes so that the government can purchase a present for them. Unfortunately for Sanders, alchemy doesn't quite exist, so many plan to cut out the middleman and purchase their own Christmas delights.

With no clear solution in mind, and Congress deciding on this issue in days, many last-minute plans and complaints have arisen. Secretary Hillary Clinton has said America should "Trump down on this Trumped-up Christmas"—whatever that means—by helping fund a second round of recount votes. "Third time's the charm!" is the secretary's new motto. The internet festers with satirical comments on America's state, and talk shows have already begun comedic roasts of anyone involved in this debacle. But by far the best reaction is from current President Barack Obama, also known as that person everybody forgot was still in the White House. Obama, seeming to enjoy his last days in the presidency and taking all the turmoil in stride, simply said this: "Whatever the case, the sun will come out tomorrow. Besides, before Kris Kringle arrives, we should probably make ourselves . . . present-able. It's a gift, really, to have this time to reflect. We can sleigh this monster of a problem and let reason reign. If we work together as Americans and become more bipolar, we can win. Because when the American people set out to conquer any tough obstacle, there really is snow contest."

Despite Obama's cringe-inducing pun spree, truth can be found in his speech—but succeeding in it will take more than ten days. So this Christmas, be pleased that Saint Nicholas may not be coming—if he did, we'd probably all get coal anyway.

JORI DUDZIKOWSKI, ***liam***, Grade 12, Age 17, Avon High School, Avon, CT.
Sara Glick, *Educator*

ABOUT THE AUTHORS

When encountered in the wild, **SARAH BALDINO** may be found napping, chasing butterflies, or wandering the streets like J. Alfred Prufrock. If you get the rare opportunity to spot her outside of her den (bed) before midday, stay at a safe distance unless you have prepared a peace offering of green tea.

SAIRA BHATTI has asked for a sword nearly every year for her birthday. She has since discovered that the pen is mightier.

DANIEL BLOKH is the author of the memoir *In Migration* (BAM! Publishing 2016) and the chapbook *Grimmening* (forthcoming from Diode Editions). He's bad at taking naps, which sucks, because he really needs a nap right now. He still hasn't figured anything out.

ANNIE CASTILLO is a poet growing up in a small town where nothing ever happens. When not napping or writing, she gets angry about bee extinction, tries to revive her desk succulent, and struggles to instill a love of etymology in anyone who will listen.

From morning sunlight winking through leaves to shadowy moonlight dancing on water, **EMMA CHAN** paints pictures with words to find herself hidden among the colors. The world is her canvas, her thoughts and feelings her paint, and her masterpiece her very own story.

CARISSA CHEN is an artist, writer, and poet of computer code. She grew up with a lisp; art and writing gave her a voice. Her work has been featured in the White House and the Kennedy Center Hall of Nations. She creates, reads, codes, and writes because she believes designing a better future requires compassion for the past.

SHANG CHEN wakes up at 1:00 p.m. and breaks his fast with a heaping pile of five egg whites, a glass of orange juice, a protein shake, and two slices of whole wheat toast. While indulging in mankind's greatest pleasure (eating), he skims through his water-damaged copy of *Zen and the Art of Motorcycle Maintenance*, jotting down ideas for future writing pieces.

BEN CONNOR is a playwright and author who calls himself a playwright and author because it makes him sound accomplished. He is, in fact, not. On the bright side, Ben can juggle and play the piano (though not simultaneously) and is probably a bigger fan of *The West Wing* than you are.

When other kids said they wanted to be an astronaut or a ballerina, **CAROLINE COOK** always said that she wanted to be an author. Words remain the outlet for a fraction of the stream of antics in her head. She is always armed with what some have deemed "too many pens."

TAYLOR CRAYTON is a young writer from New Orleans who will be attending Tuskegee University in Alabama with a focus in psychology. She has written a narrative poetry collection titled *Ugly* and plans to write another manuscript in the next five years. She has been published in the literary magazines *street* and *Transition*.

ALYSON DEL PINO lives in Miami, Florida, where the humid heat feels not like a suffocating grip but like a loving embrace. After eighteen years of writing, sweating, and listening to palm trees whisper in the breeze, she will move to chilly Philadelphia to attend the University of Pennsylvania.

SARAH FERGUSON, of Riverview, Florida, is proud to say that she is perfectly normal . . . unless you were to look at her bookshelves, where you can find three complete sets of Harry Potter and way too many books by Edgar Allan Poe. Although she spends most of her day on the marching band field, her heart dreams of storytelling and being sorted into Ravenclaw.

I spy with my little eye . . . **ANUVA GOEL**. Anuva can be found in her white lab coat and nitrile gloves, handling a test tube of DNA, or she can be found at her desk, typing away another article for her school newspaper. Sometimes she may be hard to find, but she is easily distinguished by her kindhearted spirit, helping hand, and ebullient smile!

TALIA GORDON writes because she is in love with the way words sound. She spends most of her time reading, thinking about grammar, and telling herself that she should probably pick up a pen. As a result, she is beginning to wonder if language makes any sense at all.

SETH GOZAR uses his writing to explore the faults, regrets, and fears other people hold (and his own, when he's brave enough). He owes this all to *The Little Prince* by Antoine de Saint-Exupéry. Put it on your reading list. Pass it on. You won't regret it.

DANIELLE GRUBER loves taking on challenges. Whether it is solving an intricate math problem or delving into a controversial or emotional topic in her writing, she tries to find ways to push herself to the next level.

SAMUEL HARRIS (no, not that one) is a carbon-based meat bag who has far overstayed his welcome in this universe and should probably be getting back to his home timeline by now. He likes Godzilla, *Doctor Who,* Dungeons & Dragons, Kanye West, and obsessing over the number 42. In his spare time, Sam wonders why everyone thinks he can have spare time, seeing as time is not a set of objects.

When **ALI HASSANI** isn't frantically searching Yelp for good German restaurants or fantasizing about having a Coke with Frank O'Hara, he writes. He spent his childhood in Dubai, then moved to New Hampshire to attend boarding school. In September, he starts his freshman year at Columbia University.

KRUPA HEGDE is an avid reader and writer, not only for the joy it brings her, but also to tell people she's a logophile (the look of confusion on people's face gives her great joy). She loves penning the experiences of others; that way she can have adventures without having to move at all.

JENNIFER HORSBURGH also answers to Astrian (preferred name) and "that odd anarcho-socialist" (also accurate). She is most often found ranting, writing, performing slam poetry, listening to music, or stuck on the train. She is headed from the frying pan of high school into the fire of college, from which she hopes to emerge with better tools for revolution.

DAVID HOU (nicknamed "Duck" by his U.S. history teacher) spends a lot of time sitting in front of a piano with pages of music by Chopin, Beethoven, and other deceased composers. He does this while thinking about that night's dinner. David's stomach growls equally for writing and attempting to put together tangible sentences.

When she's not writing, **ALEXANDRA KARAIM** is practicing tenor saxophone, painting, reading Cormac McCarthy, or listening to jazz. Next year, she'll attend the University of Southern California to study writing for screen and TV, combining her love for visual art and the written word.

AMIR KHADAR is a multidisciplinary artist and activist. Through creating visual art and by writing, Amir finds an outlet to speak to issues shunned by the mainstream media and practice authentic self-expression. Amir will be attending the Maryland Institute College of Art in fall 2017.

MASFI KHAN enjoys eating desserts, singing songs off-key, and worrying too often. She writes poetry to revel in the messiness and beauty of living. She knows that tomorrow will always be a mystery.

CHLOE KIM is an aspiring writer and avid animal rights activist. In the past she's worked for numerous school publications, attended the Iowa Young Writers Studio, and worked as a poetry editor for *The Adroit Journal*. She will continue her writing career at Stanford University starting this fall.

CHRISTINA LEWIS feels like she is missing out because she has yet to be stung by a bee or wasp. She has a special place in her heart for Special K cereal, songs sung in Irish, and inspirational quotes from Pinterest.

KELLEY LIU, a junior, attends Troy High School in Troy, Michigan. A graduate of the Iowa Young Writers' Studio, his writing has been recognized by various literary organizations. Kelley enjoys anything cold and is proud to say he has all 32 of his teeth.

JULIET LUBWAMA spends her days and nights reading Maya Angelou and being amazed by the wisdom of Angelou's poetry. To her, writing is a process of bravery and discovery—you never know how a poem will end until you finish it. She hopes to write both a novel and a poetry chapbook in the near future.

As an avid lover of words, **MEHREEN PASHA** spends her summers jotting down phrases that form twisted spools of dental floss in her mind. When not vigorously typing on her MacBook, she enjoys running, oil painting, and working in science labs.

ABEY PHILIP can be found on any given morning eating much more than the recommended serving size for his Reese's Puffs cereal. He can also be found coordinating with the U.S. State Department in Zagreb, Croatia, about his youth program, or binge-watching *House of Cards* on Netflix.

LINDSAY PIERCE writes because otherwise she'd scream all the time, and she likes saving her inner angry black girl for the ones who really need it. She is 5'10", plays soccer and lacrosse but not basketball, thank you for asking, and enjoys biology. She has no idea what she wants to do with her life, but she's crossed math off the list, so at least she's getting somewhere.

Impassioned writer by day and voracious reader by night, **GAYATRI RAJAN** adores the heart-stopping, blood-racing, spine-tingling craft of writing. Her dearest friends are characters in books—Green's cynical Hazel, Orwell's inquisitive Winston, and a universe of others. In addition to writing, she enjoys playing violin, dancing, painting, crocheting, and computer programming.

JAMISON RANKIN stays up until the sun rises above the trees—most of the time to hone his poetry and nonfiction. Then he sleeps until early evening, or until he has to go to work. In his spare time, Jamison enjoys the outdoors: hunting, fishing, and long walks off of short piers. Some of Jamison's work will also be appearing in *The Missouri Review.*

SAGE ROBINSON loves to write poetry and read romance novels, but she also has a deep passion for music. She plays piano and creates songs. She plans to graduate high school a year early and study creative writing at a university in California.

Upon the request for an "About the Author" blurb, **ALEXA RUSSELL** promptly took a nap and began stressing out about the accumulation of knickknacks in her bedroom, which was quite the reflection of her creative process. It may not be the most efficient process, but hey, she has won a medal or two.

SAMINA SAIFEE is constantly inspired and consumed by the intense fantasy novels she reads and the dramas she can't help but binge-watch. She plays guitar, sings, and makes a mean turkey sandwich. She's all about creativity, and will study filmmaking at New York University's Tisch School of the Arts this fall.

Among **CAMILA SANMIGUEL**'s reading material of choice: 19th-century Russian literature, a wide assortment of poetry, and passive-aggressive political swordplay on social media. Among her writings: poems she likes to describe as fervent pieces of literary activism.

LYDIA SHAW writes to make people think and to remind herself and others that they are not alone. She possesses two enormous bookcases filled with every type of book one can think of, and she is quite desperately in need of another.

DANIELLE SHERMAN is a dog lover and avid reader. She hopes to pursue a career in writing as an author, playwright, or editor. In the meantime, she enjoys soccer, nature, and art.

HAZEL THOMAS is an avid lover of sci-fi and fantasy and spends most of her time on the couch with her fiction of choice. Although she has more than plenty to say, she is admittedly too lazy to put it in words more often than not.

ANTHONY VU is grateful to be typing this, as scientists have yet to invent the imaging technology required to read the microscopic handwriting that matches his diminutive size. In the future, he will be sorely disappointed to discover he is not receiving a sizable inheritance and will be forced to list his occupation as "starving artist."

SUSAN WIE invented Netflix, rediscovered the velociraptor, danced with Joe Biden, wakeboarded on Mars (yes, there is water), and crowd-surfed at Coachella, all before the age of eighteen. She also has a small habit of embellishing the truth (except when she writes as a journalist).

ALIXANDRA WILENS sees being a writer as more of an identity than a profession. She takes on topics ranging from fantasy to feminism, and she loves to explore the stories of the past. Alixandra is an avid reader, a dog lover, and an unapologetic idealist.

Inspired by spoken-word poets such as Kai Davis and Porsha Olayiwola, **DAQUON WILSON** uses poetry for social commentary and activism. He loves giving back to his community by providing a voice for those who are commonly underrepresented. He plans to further develop his craft as he attends Emory University, starting in fall 2017.

Out of her thirteen years of life, **ESTELLA ZHOU** has spent exactly 5 years, 151 days, and 19.44 hours sleeping; the amount of time in 601 days writing; approximately 2,555 days playing music; half of the remaining time worrying about unimportant things; and the other half drifting in the vast land of imagination, where words hang from the trees like heavy fruits and broken-winged lines of poetry fall to her feet and resurrect themselves into cities.

More often than not, **SARA ZOROUFY** can be found perched in a sunny nook in her garden with a cup of tea and a tall stack of books. She tries to spend as much time as she can observing the quiet beauty of the world around her and delights in the challenge of capturing its essence in words.

EDUCATORS LIST

Ross Abrams
Hastings High School
Hastings-on-Hudson, NY

Isabel Aguirre-Kelly
Choate-Rosemary Hall School
Wallingford, CT

Champneys Atlee
Lawrenceville School
Lawrenceville, NJ

Karen Beach
Valley Christian High School
San Jose, CA

Stephanie Bennett
Pryor High School
Pryor, OK

Carla Brabham
Richland One Middle College High School
Columbia, SC

Candace Brobst
Parkland High School
Allentown, PA

Jill Burdick-Zupancic
Thomas Jefferson High School for Science and Technology
Alexandria, VA

Cheryl Burghardt
Fridley High School
Fridley, MN

Frances Cassa
Suncoast High School
Riviera Beach, FL

Erik Chaput
Lawrenceville School
Lawrenceville, NJ

Bruce Coffin
Westover School
Middlebury, CT

Stephanie Cohen
Wardlaw-Hartridge School
Edison, NJ

Mara Cregan
Pittsburgh CAPA School
Pittsburgh, PA

Chelsea Dean
Milton Academy
Milton, MA

Elizabeth Dean
Phillips Exeter Academy
Exeter, NH

Jillian Denman
Mason Middle School
Mason, OH

Danielle DeTiberus
Charleston County School of the Arts
North Charleston, SC

Caitlin Donovan
Hunter College High School
New York, NY

Matt Errico
Shanghai American School-Puxi Campus
Shanghai, China

Laura Estes-Swilley
Durant High School
Plant City, FL

Leesa Fenderson
Maret School
Washington, D.C.

Michael Fieleke
Newton North High School
Newtonville, MA

Elizabeth Flaisig
Douglas Anderson School of the Arts
Jacksonville, FL

Christine Flickinger
Downingtown STEM Academy
Downingtown, PA

Dawn Forde
Adlai E. Stevenson High School
Lincolnshire, IL

Denise Foster
Adlai E. Stevenson High School
Lincolnshire, IL

Joanne Fuller
Vermont Academy
Saxtons River, VT

Nick Geary
Goose Creek High School
Goose Creek, SC

Meg Giles
Basis School-Mesa
Mesa, AZ

Anne Gisleson
New Orleans Center for
Creative Arts
New Orleans, LA

Francis Hammes
Charleston County School of
the Arts
North Charleston, SC

Beth Webb Hart
Charleston County School of
the Arts
North Charleston, SC

Mason Henderson
Maret School
Washington, D.C.

Erin Hennessy
Kent Place School
Summit, NJ

Heather Hook
Westfall High School
Williamsport, OH

Mara Hornillos
Prospect Sierra Middle School
El Cerrito, CA

Angélique Jamail
Kinkaid School
Houston, TX

Ashley Jones
Alabama School of Fine Arts
Birmingham, AL

Thomas Juvan
Westover School
Middlebury, CT

Jen Karetnick
Miami Arts Charter School
Miami, FL

Holley Kimble
Durant High School
Plant City, FL

Azar Kohzadi
Denver School of the Arts
Denver, CO

Shawn Layton
Hillsborough High School
Hillsborough, NJ

Vivian Lopez
John F. Kennedy High School
Bellmore, NY

Christian Losa
New World School of the Arts
Miami, FL

Thomas Macey
Metro Learning Center
Magnet School
Bloomfield, CT

Dana Maloney
Tenafly High School
Tenafly, NJ

Jennifer McClain
Boise High School
Boise, ID

Molly McGrath
Casco Bay High School
Portland, ME

Tiffany Melanson
Douglas Anderson School of
the Arts
Jacksonville, FL

Carly Joy Miller
George Mason High School
Falls Church, VA

Matt Miller
Phillips Exeter Academy
Exeter, NH

Tamara Miller-Dwake
Arrowhead Park Early College
High School
Las Cruces, NM

Rachel Minkowsky
Queens High School for
Sciences at York
Jamaica, NY

Rebecca Mlinek
George Washington Carver
Center for Arts & Technology
Towson, MD

Suzanne Morrison
Friends Select School
Philadelphia, PA

Melissa Moulketis
Cloonan Middle School
Stamford, CT

Robert Novak
Manhasset Senior High
School
Manhasset, NY

Sybil O'Hare
Darien High School
Darien, CT

Sheila O'Neil-Brown
Marlboro County High School
Bennettsville, SC

Kelly O'Rourke
Desert Canyon Middle School
Scottsdale, AZ

Jason Paris
Lake Oswego High School
Lake Oswego, OR

Brad Richard
Lusher Charter School
New Orleans, LA

Jessica Rivchin
Livingston High School
Livingston, NJ

Robyn Royal
Hastings High School
Hastings-on-Hudson, NY

Freya Sachs
University School of Nashville
Nashville, TN

Matthew Sadler
Detroit Country Day
Upper School
Beverly Hills, MI

Jeff Schwartz
Lake Highland
Preparatory School
Orlando, FL

Jennifer Seavey
Thomas Jefferson High School
for Science and Technology
Alexandria, VA

Kerri Severson-Stover
Central High School
Rapid City, SD

Kevin Sheh
Desert Mountain High School
Scottsdale, AZ

Diane Shires
South Pasadena High School
South Pasadena, CA

Stephen Siperstein
Choate-Rosemary Hall School
Wallingford, CT

Brianna Smale
Sanford School
Hockessin, DE

Jennifer Solomon
Sidwell Friends Upper School
Washington, D.C.

Ronda Sturdivant
Gray Middle School
Union, KY

David Sudak
University High School
Tucson, AZ

Lauren Sullivan
Village School
Great Neck, NY

Karin Tooze
George Mason High School
Falls Church, VA

Valerie Valentino
Troy High School
Troy, MI

Sylvia Vela
John B. Alexander High School
Laredo, TX

Ann Wagenhals
Castilleja School
Palo Alto, CA

Holly Walsh
Krimmel Intermediate School
Klein, TX

Melissa Walters
R. B. Chamberlin Middle School
Twinsburg, OH

Ulrike Weide
Columbia High School
Maplewood, NJ

Michele Weiner
Mt. Pleasant High School
Wilmington, DE

Natalee Whitlock
San Diego High School of International Studies
San Diego, CA

Alesia Williams
duPont Manual High School
Louisville, KY

Victoria Woodruff
St. Stephen's Episcopal School
Austin, TX

Emily Wright
Metro Learning Center Magnet School
Bloomfield, CT

Rachel Young
Mason Middle School
Mason, OH

Mike Zelazo
Riverview High School
Riverview, FL

AN EDUCATOR'S GUIDE TO *THE BEST TEEN WRITING OF 2017*

Use the works of these National Medalist teen writers to inspire discussion and guide writing exercises with students.

1. Short Story: Discussion on characterization and voice—35 minutes

Goal: Students explain how authors establish the voice of a narrator to create distinct characters who inform a reader of time, place, and mood.

Activity: Introduce the concept of a story's "voice" by having students discuss popular first-person narratives as well as close third-person narratives that are particularly different and compelling.

Next, choose a piece with highly a engaging character voice(s). As you're reading out loud, have students mark any points in the text where they notice specific character establishment through the tone of the prose, dialects, slang, humor, or other details. After you're finished, have students discuss the following:

- What does the author want us to know, or understand, about the narrator of this story?
- How does the separation of character voices establish a reliable—or unreliable—narrator?

In partners or groups, have students select a narrator and describe his or her personality. Then have them return to the text and find specific details (speech, thought, and interaction with others) to illustrate the narrator's personality and how it informs and shapes the narrative. Share student responses.

2. Short Story: Writing with focus on characterizing the narrative—35 minutes

Goal: Students restructure a narrative with another narrator, creating the same story with a different perspective.

Activity: Ask students to take on the voice of one of the other characters and tell the story from that point of view, filling in blanks that the original narrator left. Challenge students to use important characterizing details in the reading to give color to their entries.

3. Poetry: Writing with focus on form—30 minutes

Goal: Students write using different structural techniques.

Activity: Have students write two poems on one topic of their choosing. Begin with a prose poem, in which they write freely on that topic; then have them write another poem on the same topic with a focus on line breaks to emphasize changes in rhythm or highlight specific phrases. Discuss the differences after sharing the results.

4. Personal Essay/Memoir: Writing with a focus on structure and pacing—45 minutes

Goal: Students will write an organized and coherent memoir imitating the format of a *Best Teen Writing* piece.

Activity: Select a personal essay/memoir from the anthology to read out loud with your students. Talk about the format in which the memoir is written. Discuss the choices made and how those choices are inherently personal, therefore inherently suited to convey a personal essay.

Ask your students to write their own memoirs modeled after the memoir you have selected. Have the students share their work and discuss choices that each student makes, including how those choices convey something personal to the reader.

5. Genre-Shifting Exercise—40 minutes

Goal: Students will explore form's relationship to function by converting a piece in the anthology to another genre. For example, reimagine a play as a poem or a personal essay/memoir as a science fiction/fantasy piece.

Activity: Have the students choose a favorite piece in *The Best Teen Writing*, then have them reinterpret that work in another genre. Afterward, have the students compare the original to the genre-shifted piece and discuss how the same information is relayed through contrasting forms.

6. Blog Exercise—40 minutes and homework time

Goal: Students will use critical-thinking skills to offer critiques and analysis of specific works or the anthology as a whole.

Activity: Ask students to write a blog post expressing thoughts about a specific piece of their choosing. Posts will be sent to the Alliance for consideration to be included on the Alliance blog.

- Students should express their opinions, offering positive feedback or constructive criticism, on a specific work in *The Best Teen Writing*. Alternatively, they may discuss the anthology as a whole.

- Posts may be emailed to **info@artandwriting.org**, with subject line "The Best Teen Writing of 2017 Student Blog Post."

Educators: Continue the discussion! Explore with your peers even more ways in which *The Best Teen Writing of 2017* can inspire students in your classroom! Visit the Vision and Voice website, presented by the National Writing Project, at **visionandvoice.nwp.org** to learn more.

REGIONAL AFFILIATE ORGANIZATIONS

The Alliance's reach stems from our work with Affiliate Partner organizations that administer hundreds of art and/or writing regions across the country. They are responsible for bringing the Awards to local communities, educators, and students. It is because of our Affiliate Partners' extraordinary dedication that the Scholastic Awards have been able to reach more participants and provide additional opportunities for creative teenagers across the country.

NORTHEAST

Connecticut
Connecticut Art Region
Connecticut Art Education Association
University of Hartford's Hartford Art School

Delaware
Delaware Art Region
Arts Center/Gallery at Delaware State University

Delaware Writing Region
Diamond State Branch, National League of American Pen Women, Inc.

Delaware Division of the Arts and National Endowment for the Arts

District of Columbia
D.C. Metro Writing Region
Writopia Lab D.C.

Maine
Maine Art Region
Maine College of Art

Southern Maine Writing Region
The Southern Maine Writing Project at the University of Southern Maine
The Betterment Fund

Massachusetts
Massachusetts Art & Writing Region
The Boston Globe

New Hampshire
New Hampshire Art Region
The Scholastic Art Awards of New Hampshire

New Hampshire Writing Region
The National Writing Project in New Hampshire

New Jersey
Northeast New Jersey Art Region
Montclair Art Museum

New York
Central New York Art Region
CNY Art Council
M&T Charitable Foundation

Hudson Valley Art Region
Hudson Valley Art Awards
Sullivan, Dutchess, Orange, and Ulster County BOCES; Enlarged City School District of Middletown; Orange County Arts Council; Rolling V Transportation Services

Hudson-to-Housatonic Writing Region
Writopia Lab Westchester & Fairfield

New York City Art Region
Alliance for Young Artists & Writers
Parsons School of Design

New York City Writing Region
Alliance for Young Artists & Writers
Eugene Lang College of Liberal Arts

Pennsylvania
Berks, Carbon, Lehigh, and Northampton Art Region
East Central PA Scholastic Art Awards

Lancaster County Art Region
Lancaster Museum of Art

Northeastern Pennsylvania Art and Writing Region
Marywood University

Philadelphia Art Region
Philadelphia Arts in Education Partnership

Philadelphia Writing Region
Philadelphia Writing Project

Pittsburgh Art Region
North Allegheny School District & La Roche College

Pittsburgh Writing Region
Western PA Writing Project and the University of Pittsburgh School of Education

South Central Pennsylvania Art and Writing Region
Commonwealth Connections Academy

Southwestern Pennsylvania Art & Writing Region
California University of Pennsylvania

Rhode Island
Rhode Island Art Region
Rhode Island Art Education Association

Vermont
Vermont Art & Writing Region
Brattleboro Museum & Art Center

MIDWEST
Illinois
Mid-Central Illinois Art Region
Regional Scholastic Awards Council of Mid-Central Illinois
Springfield District 186; Springfield Art Association

Suburban Chicago Art Region
Downers Grove North and South High Schools
Community High School District 99

Southern Illinois Art Region
John R. and Eleanor R. Mitchell Foundation/Cedarhurst
Center for the Arts

Indiana
Central/Southern Indiana Art & Writing Region
Clowes Memorial Hall, Butler University, and Hoosier
Writing Project at IUPUI

Kansas
Eastern Kansas Art Region
Mark Arts

Elizabeth B. Koch; K.T. Wiedemann Foundation, Inc.

Western Kansas Art Region
The Western Kansas Scholastic Art Awards
Western Kansas Scholastic Art Association

Michigan
Michigan Thumb Art Region
College for Creative Studies
Macomb Community College

Southeastern Michigan Art Region
College for Creative Studies

West Central Michigan Art and Writing Region
Kendall College of Art and Design, Ferris State University

Minnesota
Art Educators of Minnesota
Regis Center for Art; Weisman Art Museum of the University of Minnesota

Minnesota Writing Region
Minnesota Writing Project
Minnesota Council of Teachers of English

Missouri
Missouri Art Region
Kansas City Art Institute

Missouri Writing Region
Greater Kansas City Writing Project
Missouri Writing Projects Network; Missouri Council of Teachers of English

Nebraska
Nebraska Art Region
Omaha Public Schools Art Department

North Dakota
North Dakota Art Region
Plains Art Museum and the Red River Valley Writing Project at NDSU

North Dakota Writing Region
The Red River Valley Writing Project at NDSU and Plains Art Museum

Ohio
Central Ohio Art Region
Columbus College of Art & Design

Cuyahoga County Art and Writing Region
The Cleveland Institute of Art
Cuyahoga Arts and Culture

Lorain County Art Region
Lorain County Regional Scholastic Arts Committee
Nordson Corporation Foundation; Lorain County Community College Foundation; The Stocker Center Foundation

Miami Valley Art Region
K12 Gallery & TEJAS

Northeast Central Ohio Art Region
Kent State University at Stark

Northeastern Ohio Art Region
Youngstown State University and Akron Children's Hospital
Mahoning Valley
Boardman Rotary, Home Savings, First Energy, BOC
Hydraulics, Trumbull County ESC

South Dakota
South Dakota Art & Writing Region
The University of South Dakota

Wisconsin
Southeast Wisconsin Scholastic Writing Region
Southeast Wisconsin Scholastic Writing Region
Harborside Academy, Carthage College, University of
Wisconsin–Parkside

Wisconsin Art Region
The Milwaukee Art Museum
The Heller Family in memory of their parents, James K. and
Avis M. Heller; James and Carol Wiensch; Vanguard Comput-
ers, Inc. and CompURent, and an anonymous donor

Wisconsin Writing Region
Still Waters Collective

SOUTHEAST
Florida
Broward Art Region
Young at Art Museum

Hillsborough Art and Writing Region
Hillsborough County Public Schools
Suncoast Credit Union Foundation, Tampa Bay Lightning,
and Hillsborough Education Foundation

Miami-Dade Art Region
Miami-Dade County Public Schools
Rubell Family Collection

Miami-Dade Writing Region
Miami Writes
The Miami-Dade County Fair & Exposition

Northeast Florida Art Region
Northeast Florida Art Education Association
Duval County Public Schools

Palm Beach Art Region
Educational Gallery Group (Eg2)
Mary D. Fisher; The Armory Art Center; Marjorie Fisher

Pinellas Art Region
Pinellas County Art Region
Raymond James; Suncoasters of St. Petersburg; Pinellas County Schools

Sarasota Art Region
Sarasota County Schools
Sarasota County Board of Education, Ringling College of Art & Design

Georgia
Georgia Art and Writing Region
Savannah College of Art and Design

Kentucky
Louisville Metropolitan Area Art Region
Jefferson County Public Schools
Fund for the Arts, KMAC Museum, Louisville Area Fiber

and Textile Artists, Louisville Visual Art, and University of Louisville Hite Art Institute

Northern Kentucky Writing Region
Northern Kentucky Writing Region

South Central Kentucky Art & Writing Region
Southern Kentucky Performing Arts Center (SKyPAC)

Mississippi
Mississippi Art Region
Mississippi Museum of Art

Mississippi Writing Region
The Eudora Welty Foundation
C Spire Foundation

North Carolina
Eastern/Central North Carolina Art Region
Barton College

Mid-Carolina Art & Writing Region
Charlotte-Mecklenburg Schools

Western North Carolina Art Region
Asheville Art Museum
Asheville Area Section of the American Institute of Architects

Tennessee
Middle Tennessee Art Region
Cheekwood Botanical Garden and Museum of Art
The Tennessee Credit Union

Virginia

Arlington County Art Region
Arlington County Public Schools

Fairfax County Art Region
Fairfax County Public Schools

Southwest Virginia Art Region
The Fine Arts Center for the New River Valley
The Pulaski County Patriot; Southwest Times

SOUTHWEST

Arizona

Arizona Art & Writing Region
Young Authors of Arizona

Louisiana

North-Central Louisiana Writing Region
Northwestern State University Writing Project

Southeast Louisiana Writing Region
Greater New Orleans Writing Project
The Clayton-Royer Family Fund

New Mexico

New Mexico Art Region
New Mexico Art Education Association

Oklahoma

Tulsa Community College School of Visual and Performing Arts
Tulsa Community College Foundation; Ziegler Art and Frame; Arts and Humanities Council of Tulsa

Texas
Harris County Art and Writing Region
Harris County Department of Education
Texas Art Supply, Midtown Arts & Theater Center Houston: MATCH

San Antonio Art Region
SAY Sí (San Antonio Youth Yes)

Travis County Art Region
St. Stephen's School

West Texas Art Region
Wayland Baptist University and the Abraham Family Art Gallery
Plainview Cultural Arts Council, Inc.

WEST
Alaska
Alaska Art & Writing Region
Young Emerging Artists, Inc.

California
Northern California Art Region
Community Memorial Museum of Sutter County

Colorado
Colorado Art Region
Colorado Art Education Association

Hawaii
Hawai'i Art Region
Hawai'i State Department of Education
Hawai'i State Foundation on Culture and the Arts

Idaho
Idaho Writing Region
Boise State Writing Project

Nevada
Northern Nevada Art Region
The Nevada Museum of Art

Southern Nevada Art & Writing Region
Springs Preserve

Oregon
Oregon Art Region
Oregon Art Education Association
Pacific Northwest College of Art, Portland Art Museum, Oregon State University, Central Oregon Community College and Little Bird Arts

Washington
Snohomish County Art Region
Schack Art Center
City of Everett Cultural Arts Commission, Everett Public Schools, the Boeing Company, and Wells Fargo

Washington State Art and Writing Region
Cornish College of the Arts

MULTI-STATE REGIONS
Iowa Multi-State Art and Writing Region
The Connie Belin & Jacqueline N. Blank International Center for Gifted Education and Talent Development, University of Iowa

University of Iowa School of Art and Art History,
The Grant Wood Art Colony, and the Iowa City UNESCO
City of Literature

Mid-South Art Region
Memphis Brooks Museum of Art
The Brooks Museum League

Northeast Indiana and Northwest Ohio Art and Writing Region
Fort Wayne Museum of Art
PNC Bank, Boyden & Youngblutt, Indiana Tech, Lawrence
Building Corp., News-Sentinel, Northeast Indiana Public Radio

Northwest Indiana and Lower Southwest Michigan Art Region
South Bend Museum of Art

Southern Ohio, Northern Kentucky, and Southeastern
Indiana Art Region
Art Academy of Cincinnati

Twin Tiers Art Region
Arnot Art Museum
Community Foundation of Elmira-Corning and the Finger
Lakes; Chemung Canal Trust Company; New York State
Council on the Arts; Chemung County; Town of Horseheads;
Anderson Foundation; ARTS Council of the Southern Finger
Lakes; Tripp-Rose Endowment Fund

ACKNOWLEDGEMENTS

The Alliance for Young Artists & Writers gratefully acknowledges the thousands of educators who encourage students to submit their works to the Scholastic Art & Writing Awards each year and the remarkable students who have the courage to put their art and writing before panels of renowned jurors. We would like to especially recognize the National Writing Project for its far-reaching efforts in the writing community and its continued commitment to our program. In addition, our mission is greatly furthered through special partnerships with the National Writing Project, National Art Education Association, the Association of Independent Colleges of Art and Design, and the NAACP's ACT-SO program.

THANK YOU TO OUR SPONSORS

We express our sincere gratitude to Lindenmeyr Book Publishing Papers for donating the very paper these pages are printed on. Lindenmeyr also donated the paper for the 2017 Scholastic Art & Writing Awards National Catalog.

Special thanks to: Scholastic Inc., The Maurice R. Robinson Fund, Command Web Offset Co., The New York Times, New York Life Foundation, Kramer Levin Naftalis & Frankel LLP, The Herb Block Foundation, Blick Art Materials & Utrecht Art Supplies, RBC Capital Markets, Gedenk Movement, Golden Artist Colors, Neiman Marcus, Garcia Family Foundation, Bloomberg Philanthropies, ESA Foundation, Jacques & Natasha Gelman Foundation, Creative Circle, Amazon Literary Partnership, the National Endowment for the Arts, New York City Department of Cultural Affairs, and numerous other individual, foundation, and corporate funders; and, for the National Student Poets Program, the Institute of Museum and Library Services, the President's Committee on the Arts and the Humanities, and the Library of Congress.

SUPPORT THE SCHOLASTIC ART & WRITING AWARDS

Help support the Awards today! Your support will go a long way toward making the Scholastic Awards available for future generations of creative teens. Visit **artandwriting.org/donate** to make a tax-deductible contribution online, or send your gift to Alliance for Young Artists & Writers, 557 Broadway, New York, NY 10012. Thank you!